THE FRIENDS OF
JOHN GERARD

(1545–1612)

SURGEON AND BOTANIST

BY

ROBERT H. JEFFERS, N.D.H., F.L.S.

PUBLISHED BY THE HERB GROWER PRESS
FALLS VILLAGE, CONNECTICUT
1967

MADE   AND   PRINTED   IN   ENGLAND   BY
THE   ESSEX   TELEGRAPH   PRESS,   LTD.,
COLCHESTER,   ESSEX

THE FRIENDS OF
JOHN GERARD
1545–1612
SURGEON AND BOTANIST

JUST OVER NINETY years ago Dr. B. Daydon Jackson made the first attempt to write a biography of John Gerard the Elizabethan surgeon and botanist, based on original research, and issued it privately, prefixing reproductions of the two catalogues issued by Gerard in 1596 and 1599 listing the plants which he grew in his famous garden in Holborn. Since then, the late Dr. Charles E. Raven has reviewed Gerard's botanical work so far as it relates to the British flora. As many others have done, he noted the charm of the pages in Gerard's monumental work, *The Herball, or Generall Historie of Plantes*, published in 1597. In after years it was the means by which men were introduced to a study of plants. Their number included Sir Joseph Banks, Bt., President of the Royal Society.

It is not a little unfortunate that some years after his death, John Gerard was represented to be untrustworthy, both as a botanist and an author, a view which has coloured many references to him since. This present study is intended to provide a factual account of Gerard, and of many of his friends and acquaintances. Its author, ROBERT H. JEFFERS, received a training in horticulture and botany in the Gardens of the Royal Horticultural Society at Wisley, and at the Royal Botanic Garden, Edinburgh, and has published papers in the *Journal of the Royal Horticultural Society* and in the *Proceedings of the Linnean Society of London*.

Introduction

A CLASSIC WORK on printed herbals from the pen of Dr. Agnes Arber, appeared at Cambridge in 1928, since when the already voluminous literature relating to these fascinating and important works has expanded. It includes papers wherein a careful botanical examination has been made of the plants described in their pages, as a consequence of which Linnaean binomials have been provided for a large number of the plants. This was done by Linnaeus himself, in the first instance, and has been continued since his time. Thereby the plants described by the early authors of herbals have become more readily intelligible to the modern reader.

Attention of this kind has been given to *The Herball*, of John Gerard, (1545–1612), surgeon of London, published there in 1597, but the literature relating to it is extensive and lies scattered in the pages of books, and of medical, botanical and horticultural journals. There is also a certain literature of a bibliographical nature. Over the years, progress has been made in the identification of the plants that Gerard described and figured, and of the many men and women mentioned in his book. A biography of Gerard, appeared in the *Dictionary of National Biography* in 1908, before which Dr. Benjamin Dayton Jackson, for many years General Secretary of the Linnean Society of London, published privately in 1876, a biography of Gerard prefaced to a catalogue of the plants which Gerard grew in his garden in Holborn. Since then, additional material relating to Gerard has been published. This book is based mainly on biographical details of John Gerard, of the men and women mentioned in *The Herball*, as well of those with whom he is otherwise known to have had contact, including a number of his professional colleagues.

An attempt is made to suggest a possible time at which Gerard began to write *The Herball*, and to describe the circumstances attending its assembly, as well as to indicate the principal sources from which it was derived.

Gerard's extensive journeys throughout England are partially reconstructed, but no attempt is made to pass final judgement upon his botanical work, the primary aim being to provide a factual basis upon which his merit may be assessed. The inferences made from the facts recorded are confined to such deductions as one may reasonably make from them.

Without an adequate knowledge of Gerard's own life, of the lives of his many friends and acquaintances, and some other of his contemporaries, his work can be neither properly understood, nor its value correctly assessed. For that reason some facts relating to Gerard, his friends and acquaintances, as well as of certain contemporaries are set out here in chronological sequence. It has been impossible to examine Gerard's botanical work in sufficient detail, for which reason it is not discussed. To that extent, this book is not a fully rounded portrait of Gerard, but in preparing it an examination was made of a large number of the Latin plant names employed in *The Herball*, and their origin traced. This showed that Gerard's botanical work was soundly based.

All the men and women to whom he referred are traceable in contemporary records, and his references to them have been found correct. This should afford further confidence in him as an accurate observer and recorder. From the time of Theophrastus onwards, despite the gaps occurring in surviving records, there was a slow, but continuous study of plants and plant names right down to Elizabethan times. To this work Gerard's studies were necessarily related and attention is directed to this point.

Unhappily, long after Gerard's death, adverse comment upon his conduct as an author and botanist made its appearance. How this came to pass is set down in a chronological sequence that its origin and nature may be better understood. It was closely associated with the second edition of *The Herball*, published in 1633, edited, much enlarged and amended by Thomas Johnson, (*c.* 1595–1644), an apothecary of London. The circumstances attending the preparation of that edition are described.

Part I: 1545—1631

IN THE FIRST quarter of the nineteenth century, John Shepherd, the first Curator of the Liverpool Botanic Garden, set out from Liverpool in the direction of Ince. The fact is recorded in the *English Flora* of Sir James Edward Smith. One knows not if John Shepherd was ever in Ince itself, which lies on the south-eastern outskirts of Wigan, Lancashire, and there are two parts to it—Higher Ince and Lower Ince, which together constitute Ince-in-Makerfield. Late in the fourteenth century, John Gerard settled there. He was the youngest of the three sons of Sir Peter Gerard, Kt., of Bryn, Lancashire, who died in 1381. John Gerard was consequently styled as of Bryn, but after his marriage to Ellen de Ince, daughter and heiress of Richard de Ince and Aspull, he was styled John Gerard of Ince. He was descended from Rhys-ap-Tewdr-Mawr, (or Rhys the Great), King of South Wales in the eleventh century, of whom, by a collateral branch, Gerald de Barri, better known as Giraldus Cambrensis, the historian, had also been a descendant.

After his marriage, John Gerard impaled the arms of Gerard of Bryn, with those of Ince of Ince-in-Makerfield, but his son and heir, William Gerard of Ince, quartered the arms of Gerard with those of Ince. Down to 1593, he had six or seven successors in the direct male line, the house of Gerard of Ince being represented in 1593 by Miles Gerard of Ince. At some unknown point in this line of succession, a collateral branch developed from which descended John Gerard, (1545–1612), citizen and surgeon of London, who distinguished himself as a botanist and horticulturist.

The son of William Gerard of Ince, was Thomas Gerard of Ince, who, in 1458, married Elizabeth, daughter of William Norres of Speake. Their son and heir, William Gerard of Ince, married Elizabeth Biron, daughter of John Biron of Biron, whereby he became the ancestor of the family of Gerard of Harrow-on-the-Hill, Middlesex; of the Gerards who were Barons, Gerard of Gerard's Bromley, Staffordshire; and of the Gerards who were later Barons of Brandon, and Earls of Macclesfield. The first of these two noble families was founded during the lifetime of John Gerard, surgeon and botanist, who was closely related to the main line of Gerard of Ince, since his shield of arms and crest were precisely those of Gerard of Ince. He quartered the arms of Gerard of Ince, with those of Ince

9

of Ince, but bore a crescent for difference, a heraldic device indicating that he was not of the main line itself. As he does not seem to have been the recipient of a grant of arms and crest, one may infer that he inherited them from his father. Unfortunately it has been impossible to establish his precise relationship to the main line of Gerard of Ince, nor has it been possible to ascertain his parentage, yet it is clear that he was a member of a large and illustrious family, whose members had rendered, and continued to render distinguished service in England. It seems to have been the case that his father had settled in Cheshire early in the sixteenth century, as John Gerard, surgeon and botanist was born in that county about 1545, two years before the death of Henry VIII. It is likely that his father was living then in the vicinity of Wistaston, Cheshire, at that time a village, as it was there that Gerard went to school, passing on his way, a wood wherein raspberries grew wild as he recalled in later-life. Wistaston was situated two miles north-east of Nantwich, in the southern part of Cheshire. Though some biographers have stated that Gerard was born in Nantwich, it is unlikely that his birth took place in Nantwich itself, but as it was the nearest town to Wistaston he would have been familiar with it at an early age, and seems to have maintained contact with some of its inhabitants later in life.

No details are available of Gerard's school-days, but as he was in later-life proficient in Latin, one may assume that he was grounded in Latin in Wistaston, the Roman authors studied being, generally, Terence, Caesar, Cicero, Virgil, Sallust, Horace and Ovid in the schools of the time. Gerard was afterwards found familiar with the writings of some of these men. He decided to enter upon the career of a surgeon, and was apprenticed, in 1562, aged sixteen, to Alexander Mason, barber-surgeon of London, which involved his father in the payment of fees to cover the cost of food and clothing, but Gerard had to attend for a personal interview in London before the indentures were signed, and provide proof that he could read and write.

Alexander Mason was particularly eminent in his profession, and had a large practice in London. He had become a member of the United Company of Barber-Surgeons of London, which had been incorporated in 1540, and was a member of the Livery. He had served the office of Second Warden in 1556, and while Gerard was still his apprentice he was elected Master of the Company in 1567.

10

Despite earlier attempts to introduce them, no true technical standards for a surgeon had existed in England until 1540, when the United Company of Barber-Surgeons received its Charter. By the time Gerard became an apprentice there was a prescribed course of reading for apprentices, who also attended weekly lectures on surgery, and set courses of lectures on anatomy and dissections given by the Company's Reader in Anatomy. The period of apprenticeship was the statutory one of seven years, at the end of which apprentices were examined by a Court of thirteen Examiners, including the Master of the Company. A successful apprentice received a License to practice Surgery and was admitted a Freeman of the Company.

Such was the general character of the training Gerard underwent, and it is instructive to notice the set books of study. They were the *De Methodo Medendi* of Galen; the *Anatomy*, (1530), of Realdus Columbus; Tagaultius; the *Chirurgerye*, (1543), of John of Vigo; and the *Questiones*, (1544), of Guido, of which an English translation was available. Gerard may also have had to read the books of Thomas Vicary, (d. 1561), the first Master of the Company. Other books on surgery included *Book Six* of Paulus Aegineta, an author whom Gerard later quoted, and the last two books of Celsus, but these existed in Latin translation only, in which form Gerard may have read Aegineta. Most ordinary surgeons had to make do with *De Chirurgica*, of John of Arderne, and the *Chirugia Magna*, of Guy de Chauliac. It is clear that a grounding in Latin was an essential prerequisite for an intending surgeon. Gerard is not known to have attended any school other than that at Wistaston, Cheshire, before coming to London, so one may assume that Latin was among the subjects taught there. From the circumstance that Gerard, later in life, also included a little Greek in *The Herball*, one may infer that, between 1562 and 1597, he perhaps acquired a smattering of that language, so that it seems probable that his training under Alexander Mason was above the average.

It is curious that a surgeon could know Latin, yet could still be considered no scholar, but it was this that prevented him from attaining the same social status as a physician, though it did not prohibit him from commanding good fees. This comparatively "unlettered" state debarred him from direct access to the writings of the Greeks, while the physicians also opposed the writing of vernacular medical texts, curtailed the curriculum of a surgeon, and prohibited the prescription of inward remedies, except in consultation.

A clear appreciation of this situation fully explains Gerard's subsequent reference to his own lack of scholarship, as well as that of his friend and fellow-surgeon, John Bennett, of Maidstone, Kent. Since *The Herball* later showed that Gerard was well read in Latin, and that he was able to translate from it into English, as well as to write in that language, one may infer that Gerard was a diligent student during his schooldays and his period of apprenticeship. He was attracted at an early age to a study of plants, of which he afforded evidence in *The Herball*.

The fact that Gerard afterwards was familiar with the work of Paulus Aegineta, is of more than passing interest. Rembert Dodoens, was born at Malines, (Mechlin), in the Southern Netherlands in 1517, educated at the University of Louvain, where he qualified as Licentiate in Medicine, and then travelled in Germany and France. Coming to Paris, he met there Jean Gunther, Professor of Medicine in the University, who had translated Paulus Aegineta. He was sufficiently impressed with Dodoens' ability as to give this translation to him, with a request that he should undertake its collation, an obligation which Dodoens duly discharged, and the work appeared as *Paulus Aegineta, a Joanne Guintero*, (Jean Gunther), *latine conversus, a Remberto Dodonaeo ad Graceum textae accurate collatus ac recensitas*. (Casilias, 1546), 8vo. This was the Latin translation of Paulus Aegineta available for study in England by intending surgeons, and had been available only since 1546, the year following Gerard's birth. If, during his apprenticeship, he studied this work, it was his first introduction to the writings of Rembert Dodoens, who, having completed his travels, settled in his native Malines, and there practised as a physician until 1574.

In the first year of Gerard's apprenticeship a book appeared in England, which, since it was directly concerned with surgery, deserves attention. The author was the Rev. William Bullein, and the title of his book, *Bullein's Bulwarke of defence against all Sicknes, Sornes, and Woundes* . . . "Doen by William Bulleyn, and ended this Marche, *anno salutis*, 1562". It was "Imprinted at London by John Kyngston", and had an engraved title-page. The copy seen was a handsomely bound one, formerly in the library of Sir Joseph Banks, Bt., F.R.S., and now in the British Museum, and in excellent condition. After the title-page was a full page reproduction of the shield of arms, motto and crest of Henry Cary, Baron Hunsdon, first cousin to Queen Elizabeth, to whom the book was dedicated, and dated "London, March, 1562". Then followed, "To the good

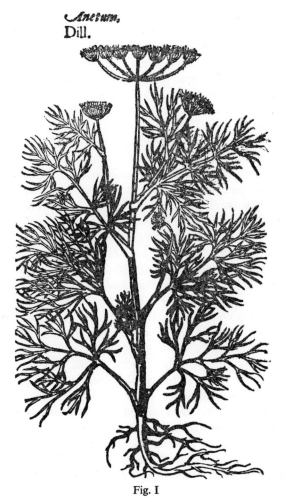

Fig. I

Anetum: Dill, "is called in Greeke *anethon;* in Latin likewise *Anethum*, and *Anetum*". (JOHN GERARD. *The Herball* (1597) p. 878.)

reader, Willyam Bulleyn sendeth Salutation", and after that was a list of "The Authors, Capitaines and Souldiours of this *Bulwarke*", totalling forty-three names, among which were Hippocrates, Galen, Avicenna, Dioscorides, Averroes, Rhazes, Jean Ruell, Theophrastus, Paulus Aegineta, Arnold de Villanova, Leonhard Fuchs, Conrad Gesner, Pier Andrea Mattioli, Strabo, Pliny, Ovid and Virgil, in that order. Then came the text, divided into five books, printed, beautifully clearly, almost entirely in Black Letter. The first book was of particular interest, as it was entitled *The Booke of Simples*, which was followed by three pages of illustrations, containing nine figures on each page, of which twenty-four depicted medicinal plants. This book ended with an alphabetical index of the simples discussed in the text. The second book was entitled, *A Little Dialogue Between Sorenes and Chyrugi*, on foilos IV to VI of which was an alphabetical list of physicians, five surgeons, and one apothecary, the earliest of whom were Aesculapius and Hippocrates, and the latest were some physicians and surgeons who were contemporary with the early years of William Bullein. It is relevant to notice that of the five surgeons, one was Thomas Gale, author of a work on surgical practice, and the other was Thomas Vickary, first Master of the Barber-Surgeons Company and also an author, as already noticed. The text concerned itself with herbal and other remedies, and ended with a list of aphorisms and an index, and was dated "March 1562". The third book had the title *The Booke of Compoundes*, and dealt with recipes for medicines. Right at the end of the text, it was noted that "few are equal in worthiness and knowledge to Thomas Gladfield, a cunning Chirurgian of London", and was followed by an alphabetical index. Book four bore the title *The Names of the Compoundes and the Apothecaries Rules*, wherein Valerius Cordus was mentioned. The text described the preparation of medicines, and this book ended with "Valeto, Guitihelmus Bullenus, Januarij *anno salutis* 1562". The fifth and last book was *The Book of the Use of Sickmen and Wholesome Medicen*, and the entire work terminated with "The ende of the Dialogue between Health and Sickness by William Bulleyn, Marcy, *anno salutis* 1562", and an index.

This was, for the time, a remarkably fine book, and Gerard may well have possessed himself of a copy of it. The text is pleasant and easy to read, and cast in the form, throughout all five books, in the form of a dialogue, between Marcellus, and Hillarius, a physician. At one place Marcellus is represented as a native of Suffolk, a county with which Hillarius declared himself familiar.

14

William Bullein spent part of his life in the same county. The *Book of Simples* well repays study for the Latin plant-names of medicinal plants recorded therein, as it reveals the state of botanical knowledge in the same year in which Gerard began his apprenticeship. These, on being extracted and examined, prove to be identical with those which occur in medieval herbals and plant-lists, and all the plants are readily identifiable. Gerard's early knowledge of Latin plant-names was thus rooted in those used in medieval manuscripts.

Definite evidence of this is afforded by the fact that Gerard was certainly familiar with the books issued from 1538 until 1568 by Dr. William Turner, wherein he laid the foundations of botany in England. Dr. Turner's published work culminated in the appearance at Cologne in 1568, the last year of Gerard's apprenticeship, of the complete edition of his *New Herball*, which was addressed to Queen Elizabeth. Its appearance was a posthumous one, as William Turner died at his house in Crutched Friars, London, in 1568 and was buried in the church of St. Olave, Hart Street.

The first part of this herbal had been published in 1551, and was revised, and the second part was issued in 1562. This edition of 1568, contained the revised version of the first part, a re-print of the second part, and to these the third part was now added. Dr. Turner's death virtually marked the end of the first period of the publication in England, or by English authors, of herbals and books on plants. Printed herbals had appeared in England since 1525, when Richard Banckes printed the first of them as *An Herbal*. This, and its successors, had been derived from the Middle English medical manuscript X90 (Stockholm), to which Dr. Gösta Brodin has given the name *Agnus Castus*. A second group of larger books, was based on a translation into English of the French work *Le Grand Herbier*, which, in turn had its ultimate roots in the writings of Albertus Magnus, (*c.* 1193–1280). A third and last group of herbals was derived from a medieval manuscript work attributed to Macer, but whose real author was Odo de Meung.

William Turner's *New Herbal*, was notable for the dedication of the third part, in the final edition of 1568, to the Company of Barber-Surgeons of London, and was dated at Wells, Somerset, 24th June, 1564. It was offered to the surgeons partly because many of its contents related to surgery, and partly because the duty had been laid upon him by Master Wright, late surgeon to the Queen. The first and second parts had dealt with plants mentioned by earlier writers, hence Turner's botanical work had been inevitably largely concerned with identification. Gerard certainly had access to a copy of this book, and may even have been the owner of a copy of it.

Gerard completed his apprenticeship in 1569, and was admitted a Freeman of the Company of Barber-Surgeons at the age of twenty-four years. The next step in his career within the Company was admission to the Livery, of which, though no record of it has survived, he may have become a member at the time of his admission to the Freedom. Thereby he became a full-member of the Company, and was ready to practise as a surgeon on his own account.

Few records appear to be available respecting Gerard's activities between 1569 and 1577, but events occurred during this period having a bearing on his subsequent career, and others may be assumed to have taken place during the same time.

Two important travellers arrived in London during 1569. They were Pierre Pena, M.D., a native of Aix, in Provence, recently in practice as a physician at Montpellier, in the south of France, and Matthias de L'Obel, M.D., a native of Lille, a qualified physician, and a French Protestant. Both men were botanists, and both had studied at the University of Montpellier under Guillaume Rondelet Pena had arrived there a month before L'Obel, who had been travelling in Italy, during which tour he made acquaintance with apothecaries in northern Italy.

Guillaume Rondelet, was a physician and distinguished as a zoologist, after whose death Pena and L'Obel made botanical collections in the south of France, particularly in Narbonne, and in part of the Pyrenees. Their appearance in London in 1569, was their first visit to England. The available evidence suggests that they had been collaborating for some time in writing a book on plants, because shortly after their arrival in London, a book appeared there of which they were joint authors. It was entitled *Stirpium Adversaria Nova* . . . Authoribus Pierre Pena et Matthias de L'Obel, Medicis", with an engraved copper-plate title-page, at the foot of which the colophon read "Londoni, 1570". The title-page was a work of some merit by a process then relatively new to England. The book was dedicated to Queen Elizabeth, and this dedication was followed by an address to the University of Montpellier, in the course of which the authors acknowledged their indebtedness to Theophrastus, Dioscorides, Pliny, Mattioli and to their contemporary, Rembert Dodoens, M.D., a physician of Mechlin, Southern Netherlands. The text consisted of 458 pages, and the book was written entirely in Latin; there were some text illustrations. At the foot of the last page (p. 458) there was printed *"Londoni, 1571, Calendis Januariis excudebat prelum Thomae Purfoetij ad Lucretie symbolum, cum gratis privilegis."* Then followed an index to the names of the plants in the text. The book had been entered at Stationer's Hall in 1569–1570.

It is important to realise that each of the authors was a botanist in his own right, though the junior author, Matthias de L'Obel, was subsequently more distinguished botanically, than the senior author, Pierre Pena. In 1571, L'Obel was the guest, at his home in Somerset, of Edward Saintloo, to whom there is reference in the book at p. 370, and in the same year L'Obel met Charles de L'Escluse in Bristol. Plants that L'Obel found in Bristol are mentioned in the book. Charles de L'Escluse was also a French Protestant botanist, who had been trained in the law, and was never a physician. Economic plants had attracted him from an early age, and he maintained his interest in them throughout life. His visit in 1571 was the first he made to England, and he made a second one in 1581. Pierre Pena executed a mission in Kent during 1571, after which year he does not appear to have been in England. Certainly his sojourn there was only short, as he returned to France and became physician to the King in Paris.

Both Pena and L'Obel were long enough in England before their book was published to survey the gardens of London, in which there are references to them. They also made the acquaintance of Thomas Penny, M.D. in London, whom they may have met earlier in Montpellier, and, in particular, of Hugh Morgan, a leading apothecary in London, with contacts with Continental apothecaries, especially those in northern Italy. Pena and L'Obel also made some observations on the English flora, references to which, as also to Thomas Penny and Hugh Morgan appeared in their book. They also knew William De Laune, M.D. and John de Franqueville. These facts suggest that the book was partly written before the authors came to England, but substantial parts were written in England, between 1569 and 1572. This would explain why the title page is dated 1570, while the date 1571 appeared on the last page. Clearly the work was completed and printed by the end of that year, and before it closed Pierre Pena probably returned to France.

Matthias de L'Obel remained in England and settled in practice as a physician in London, but was never admitted to the College of Physicians of London. It may be that he made the acquaintance of

John Gerard between 1569 and 1574. While Gerard was serving his apprenticeship, the Company of Merchant Adventurers in London, pioneered and opened up trade with Russia, which was reached by developing a north-east passage round North Cape, Norway, and in consequence of reports received, a subsidiary aim of this northern sea route was the discovery of the northern passage to Cathay, then said to exist. The pioneers of the northern passage to Russia were Richard Chancellor, Thomas Borough, and William Borough. Later, a route was opened through the Baltic to Narva, for pioneering which William Borough was responsible. The Company of Merchant Adventurers was using both routes in 1569, and in 1597 Gerard recorded that he had been in Norway, Denmark, Swevia, Poland, Narva (Estonia), and to Moscow. This shows that he took the Baltic route, which would have taken him to Bergen (Norway), Copenhagen (Denmark), Gotland (Sweden), Duntzig (Poland), and Narva (Estonia), these being the chief points of call for English ships. From Narva the journey was overland to Moscow. The suggestion that Gerard may have sailed as a ship's surgeon is not unreasonable, as it would have provided him with useful professional experience, but the Company's ships carried, as passengers, gentlemen wishing to see countries overseas, and Gerard may have been of that number, as no record is at present known of the capacity in which he made the journey. It is reasonable to assume he travelled so far as a young man, rather than later in life, probably making only one such journey. Additional factors in support of this view derive from some facts to be set out later, from which it may be inferred that between 1569 and 1577, Gerard married and settled in Holborn, a circumstance rendered the more likely from a consideration of the following facts.

Sir William Cecil, was created Baron Burghley of Burleigh in Northamptonshire, in 1570, and had gardens there, at his London residence in the Strand, and at Theobalds, Hertfordshire, an estate he had purchased in 1564. For these gardens he had been gathering plants, by means of gifts or by purchase, at home and abroad. His agent, Peter Kemp, kept him informed of the progress of planting and other estate work at Burleigh, but some time before 1577, Lord Burghley was already in need of a good man to take charge of the gardens in London and at Theobalds, and had been looking for one. By 1577, at the latest, Gerard was Superintendent of these gardens, and his association with Lord Burghley may have commenced before that year. It is clear that his selection for this responsible post involving the supervision of a collection of indigenous and exotic

Cuminum ſatiuum Dioſcoridis.
Garden Cumin.

Fig. II

Cuminum sativum Dioscoridis: Garden Cumin, sown and harvested in Italy and
Spain.   Gerard sowed it in his garden, "in the midst of May"; it germinated six
days later, and bore ripe seed at the end of July.   (JOHN GERARD.   *The Herball*
(1597) p. 907.)

19

plants, to which additions were continually being made, points to his having established himself as a cultivator of them. This would have needed a period of settled life in London to acquire, which means that he must have had a garden there of his own.

His later references to his own activities, justify the inference that Gerard made botanical excursions into Kent by 1577, and perhaps into Essex. On his Kentish excursions he may have received guidance from Hugh Morgan, the apothecary mentioned in 1570–1571 by Pena and L'Obel. The name of Hugh Morgan occurs in the registers of the parish of St. Vedast, Foster Lane, London at this time, and he practised his profession in that vicinity. Not far away, he had a garden in St. Stephen's parish, Coleman Street, which Pena and L'Obel had visited. Hugh Morgan was the son of John Morgan, of Great Bardfield, Essex and of Joan Copcott, his wife, daughter of Richard Copcott, of Buckinghamshire. He was born in about 1530, at Great Bardfield, and was an octogenarian at his death in 1616, and not a centenarian as has been recorded. His uncle, the Rev. Richard Morgan, a graduate in arts and divinity of the University of Oxford, was incumbent of Great Bardfield. Hugh Morgan served his apprenticeship as an apothecary in London, and became free of the Grocers' Company, wherein at that time the apothecaries were included. For that reason he was described as citizen and grocer, and became Apothecary to Queen Elizabeth. He married Lucy Sibbell, daughter of Nicholas Sibbell, of Farningham, Kent, younger brother of John Sibbell, of Eynsford, a village nearby, the last male heir of a family with estates in Eynsford and Farningham, long settled there. John Sibbell's daughter, Elizabeth, married Robert Bosvile, and on her father's death, she thereby, as the heiress, conveyed the estates to the Bosvile family, in which they remained for a long time afterwards. John Sibbell died in 1575, and Gerard afterwards recorded having collected plants on "Mr. Sibbell's lands at Farningham", which shows that he was there not later than 1575. Hugh Morgan may have guided him to that locality.

Between 1571 and 1574, the movements of Matthias de L'Obel cannot be reconstructed precisely, but he was probably in London during that time, and one may regard it as the first period of his association with Gerard. In 1574, L'Obel was certainly in Antwerp, and in September of that year, Rembert Dodoens left Malines to take up new duties as Physician to the Emperor Maximilian II at Vienna. On the death of the Emperor, he remained in his post under Rudolph

II until 1580. L'Obel remained in Antwerp until 1581, when he seems to have gone first to Middleburg and then to Delft, in the capacity of Physician to Prince William of Orange, but upon the Prince's assassination on 14th July, 1584, he returned to London. He was thus continuously absent from England, from 1574 until 1585, during which period no collaboration with Gerard was possible. During this long sojourn in the Netherlands, L'Obel was accompanied by his first wife, she having assisted him in collecting plants in England between 1569 and 1571. Meanwhile Gerard made more extensive excursions into Kent, one of which took him as far as Quex Park, near Birchington, the former home of Sir Henry Crispe, who, from 1558 until 1573 had been engaged in measures to secure the defence of Kent. He died in 1575, and Gerard's collections near Quex Park were made between 1575 and 1597. In connection with this area, Gerard also mentioned "a Kentish gentleman, Bartholomew Lane", whom it has not been possible to identify, but at that time a Bartholomew Lane, carried on business as a hosier in the parish of Christ Church, Newgate, London, which was no distance eastwards from Gerard's home in Holborn. Unfortunately no details are available to show that the hosier had Kentish associations. Gerard's Kentish botanical excursions gave him practical acquantance with the flora of the northern part of the county.

The first edition of Holinshed's *Chronicle* was published in London during 1577, of which a second edition appeared in 1587. It contained a notable contribution by the Rev. William Harrison entitled "A Description of England". In Book II, Chapter 20 (1587), he wrote of Gardens and Orchards, and had both a garden and an orchard at his Rectory at Radwinter, Essex, of which parish he had been incumbent since 1558, and had become Canon of Windsor in 1586. His death occurred in 1593, and he was buried at Windsor. Gerard visited the Rectory orchard at Radwinter, but made no reference to the garden or to William Harrison, which suggests that the visit was made after Harrison's death, and if so, it hints at a manuscript of *The Herball* being assembled at different dates over a period of time.

Before being presented to the Rectory of Radwinter by William Brooke, tenth Baron Cobham, William Harrison had been Domestic Chaplain to his lordship at Cobham Hall, Kent, where there were some excellent gardens. Gerard knew of them, as he collected plants near Cobham Hall.

Harrison's remarks on gardens and orchards cover vegetable crops, other crop plants, exotic plants, orchards and gardeners. He referred to rare and medicinal herbs, and of garden plants in 1587 he noted that:

> "How art also helped nature in the daily colouring, doubling and enlarging the proportion of our flowers, it is incredible to report; for so curious and cunning are our gardeners now these days, that they presume to do in manner what they list with nature, and moderate her course in things as if they were her superiors. It is a world also to see how many strange herbs, plants, and unusual fruits are daily brought unto us, from the Indies, Americas, Taprobane (Ceylon), Canary Isles and all parts of the world."

The occurrence of doubling or semi-doubling in flowers seems to have been specially appreciated from the sixteenth century onwards; the number of species known to have exhibited this phenomenon was already considerable in 1587. Sixteenth century herbals contain figures showing plants with double or semi-double flowers. Of exotic herbs in gardens, Harrison had seen three to four hundred, "of the half of whose names within forty years past we had no manner of knowledge". Their cultivation had led to some neglect of indigenous herbs.

Harrison's time limit with respect to plant names carries one back to the period of 1537–1547, which was just within that during which the earliest printed herbals appeared in England, all of which were derivations of medieval texts. William Turner began his work on plants during the same period, and his books were published between 1538 and 1568. His main work had been with identification, but Harrison made no reference to him. Instead, he touched upon the point that the exotic plants then being introduced into Western Europe from more distant lands were unknown to Greek, Roman, and medieval authors. He had referred to Sarsaparilla, Mochoacan, and the compound medicines made with foreign drugs, and returned thanks to the physicians, who tried to find out the use of simples, both indigenous and exotic, whereof:

> "The chief workman (or, as I may call him, the founder of this device) is Carolus Clusius, the noble herbarist whose industry hath wonderfully stirred them up into this good act. For albeit that Matthiolus, Rembert (Dodoens), L'Obel and others have travelled very far in this behalf, yet none hath come near Clusius, much less gone further in the finding and true descriptions of such herbs as of late are brought to light. I doubt not but if this man were in England but one seven years, he would reveal a number of herbs growing with us whereof neither our physicians nor apothecaries as yet have any knowledge. And even like thanks be given unto our nobility, gentlemen and others for their continual nutriture and cherishing of such homeborne (i.e. indigenous) and foreign simples in their gardens; for hereby they shall not only be at hand and preserved, but also their forms made more familiar to be discerned and their forces better known than hitherto they have been."

The gardens of Sir William Cecil, who had been created Baron Burghley in 1570, in London and at Theobalds, those of Sir Francis Carew at Beddington, Surrey, and those of Harrison's patron, Lord Cobham were among those contemporary horticultural works then in hand by the nobility and gentry, and in which Gerrard was a participant by his superintendence of Lord Burghley's gardens. Harrison's description of his own garden in 1587 is worth notice:

"For my own part, good reader, let me boast a little of my garden, which is but small, and the whole area thereof little above 300 foot of ground, and yet, such hath been my good luck in purchase of the variety of simples, that, notwithstanding my small ability, there are very nearly three hundred of one sort and other contained therein, no one of them being common or usually to be had. If therefore my little plot, void of all cost in keeping, be so well furnished, what shall we think of those of Hampton Court, Nonsuch, Tibaults, Cobham Garden and sundry others appertaining to divers citizens of London, whom I could particularly name, if I should not seem to offend them by such my demeanour and dealing."

Here, then, is his reason for omitting reference to several outstanding gardens then known to exist in London, with which and with their contents Gerard became familiar. He became acquainted with the gardens at Hampton Court, Middlesex, and with the Keeper of them, "Mr. Huggens", but made no reference to those at Nonsuch Palace, Ewell, Surrey. He was already supervising the gardens at Tibaults, (i.e. Theobalds), and was himself in the vicinity of Cobham Garden, by which Harrison meant the one at Cobham Hall, Kent, while these extracts from his chapter on gardens and orchards illuminate the time at which Gerard's association with Lord Burghley began.

Meanwhile, a lamentable event occurred in 1574, when Gerard's former master, Alexander Mason, died during his second term of office as Master of the Barber-Surgeons Company on 3rd April, 1574, having been active for at least eighteen years in its affairs.

Lord Burghley's association with Gerard lasted for twenty-one years, a point worth notice, nor was it affected when, on 21st February, 1578, Gerard was summoned to appear before the Court of Assistants of his Company to answer an allegation made against him by Richard James, but, upon Gerard answering that he could justify remarks he had made concerning Mrs. James, the matter was dismissed to the Common Law.

The year 1578 had really a quite different significance for Gerard, because during it, Henry Lyte, of Lytescary, Somerset, published in English a folio volume, entitled *A Niewe Herball*, which was printed in Antwerp by E. Loe, and was sold "at London, by me Gerard Dewes, dwelling in Pawle's Churchyarde, at the Signe of the Swanne, 1578". The book was dedicated to Queen Elizabeth, one thousand and fifty plants being described in its pages, of which four-fifths were illustrated with foreign blocks, which the printer in Antwerp had obtained. These blocks had been used to illustrate the *De Stirpium Historia*, (1542), of Leonhardt Fuchs, a work whose date places it among the early Continental printed herbals, which, like the early ones in England, had their roots in medieval texts, so far as the plant names were concerned, as an examination of them confirms. Gerard was later familiar with Fuchs' work, and quoted from it. To Henry Lyte's book, complimentary epigrams were contributed by the Rev. William Bullein, author of *The Bulwarke of Defence*, (London, 1562); by William Clowes, surgeon, and by the Rev. Thomas Newton, who, like Gerard, was a native of Cheshire. Bullein has been said to have been personally acquainted with all the Elizabethan botanists from Turner to Gerard, but his death in 1576, occurred at a time when Gerard's career was only just beginning, and his contribution must have been written at least two years before Henry Lyte's book was published. One may perhaps infer that Lyte's manuscript was in a very advanced stage by 1576. The other two contributors, William Clowes and the Rev. Thomas Newton, were subsequently close associates of Gerard. It is possible that besides being a professional colleague, William Clowes may have been on terms of friendship with Gerard by 1578.

A word should be said of the London bookseller, Gerard Dewes, whose name was correctly written Gherardt D'Ewes. He carried on business as a printer and bookseller, printing some thirteen books between 1552 and 1587, at the sign of The Swan in St. Paul's Churchyard. He had been admitted a Freeman of the Stationers' Company on 4th October, 1557, and became Lord of the Manor of Gaynes, in Upminster, Essex, in 1587, until his death on 12th April, 1591, when he was buried there in the parish church. Though not the printer of it, Gherardt D'Ewes was responsible for introducing Lyte's book to the English market. With its contents Gerard became familiar, and may well have been the possessor of a copy of it.

The history of Henry Lyte's book is relevant to Gerard's own work. A temporary upsurge of nationalist feeling in the Southern Provinces of the Netherlands had caused Rembert Dodoens, then in Malines, to publish at Antwerp in 1554, a book on plants written in Flemish, under the title *Herbarius Van Cruydt Boek*, printed by the house of Van Loe which had printed Henry Lyte's book. Shortly after this, Charles de L'Escluse, a French Protestant, a native of Arras, arrived in Antwerp, where he employed himself in translating the *Cruydtboek* into French. This translation appeared as *Histoire des Plantes*...Nouvellement traduit de bas Alleman en Francois (Anvers, 1557), a folio work, with text illustrations. It was from this book that Henry Lyte made his careful translation into English, and he had by him at the same time a copy of the *Cruydtboek* itself. To aid him with the plant names he utilised the *Thesaurus Linguae Romanae et Britannicae*, (London, 1563), of Thomas Cooper, afterwards Bishop of Winchester; the *New Herbal* (Cologne, 1568), of William Turner, and the *Stirpium Adversaria Nova*, (London 1570–71), of Pena and L'Obel. Lyte also incorporated some additional matter, including the habitats of some Somerset plants. On p. 174, Lyte referred to the use of *Campanula trachelium, L.*, in salads "As Pena writeth in his booke intitled *Stirpium Adversaria Nova*, Fol. 138", his co-author, L'Obel, not being mentioned. At a later time Gerard followed this practice of citing the joint work of Pena and L'Obel.

In 1580, Rembert Dodoens returned from Vienna, and settled again in Malines until he left for Leyden. From 1574 until 1581, L'Obel had practised medicine in Antwerp, and in the year 1581 was concerned there with the printer, Christopher Plantin, in producing a work, in Flemish, entitled *Kruydboeck*. It appeared at Antwerp, in 1581, in two parts, the total number of 2,181 figures being those which had been used to illustrate the work of Dodoens and de L'Escluse. At the request of Dr. Severin Gobel, Physician to the King of Denmark, Plantin assembled the figures used to illustrate the *Stirpium Adversaria Nova*, of Pena and L'Obel, and issued them in an oblong octavo volume, with names only, no text, as *Icones Plantarum*, Antwerp, 1581. These publications having been completed, L'Obel seems to have gone next, in 1581, to Middleburg, and then to Delft, returning to Antwerp in 1584 and leaving for London in 1585, as already described. During his period in the Netherlands, L'Obel acquired a figure of the true Ginger plant, (*Zinziber officinalis*, Roscoe), to replace an incorrect one that he had received earlier. Arrived in London, L'Obel settled there for the rest of his life, and soon after his return he forwarded the two figures of the ginger plant to Gerard, accompanied by a letter in Latin explaining how the two figures had come into his possession. This indicated that Gerard was acquainted with L'Obel before his departure from London in 1574, and, in *The Herball*, he reproduced the two figures, together with an English translation of L'Obel's letter.

While yet L'Obel was in the Northern Provinces of the Netherlands, Christopher Plantin issued from his press at Antwerp in 1583, the latest, and as it proved the last work of Rembert Dodoens, M.D., the physician of Mechlin (Malines), which was a folio volume of 860 pages, entitled *Stirpium Historia Pemptades Sex, Sive Libri XXX*. The copy of it in the Library of the British Museum was formerly in that of Sir Joseph Banks, Bt., P.R.S., and contains manuscript notes by Jonas Dryander, giving the names of some of the plants as they appeared in John Ray's *Synopsis*. This book was dedicated to the City Council and City of Antwerp, and received the "Summa Privilegii Caesarei", at Prague on 11th August, 1580, and the "Summa Privilegii Regis Gallianum", at Fontainbleau on 5th August, 1582. There were commendatory verses by Johannes Posthius, Jacobus D.F.P.N. Susium, and Franconis Estis Gorcomio, which were followed by Dodoens' address to the Reader in Latin, and an instructive list of the authors whose works are cited in the text, but without the titles of their books. The list was alphabetically arranged, and the names included those of Charles de L'Escluse, Matthias de L'Obel, William Turner, and also Johannes Aicholtz, Professor of Medicine at Vienna. At the end of the book were four indexes: 1 *Index Nominum Graecorum*, 2 a manuscript index to the plant names in Flemish (in this particular copy), 3 *Latinarum vocum et appellationum stirpium index*, and 4 *Arabicarum, Barbarum, et officiniis receptarum appellationum*. This was a clearly printed, well illustrated work, and with its contents Gerard became familiar, so that a brief description of its text should be given.

It was arranged in six parts, each of which had five books, making the total of thirty recorded in the title. Book I, in the first part, was entitled "*De Stirpium Generibus*", and was followed by four books devoted to "*De Abrotano; De Filipendula, De Marrubio*, and *De Ruta graveolente*". The second part was "*De Floribus Coronariis Odoratis ux Umbelliferis Herbae*", and was based on the author's "*Florum et Coronariarum odoratatrumque nonmullarum Herbarum historia*", published at Antwerp in 1568, of which a second edition had appeared at the same place in 1569. The third part dealt with roots, purgative herbs, climbing plants, deleterious and pernicious herbs, ferns, mosses and fungi, but the cryptogams were very few. This was based on the author's "*Purgantium aliarumque eo facientium*

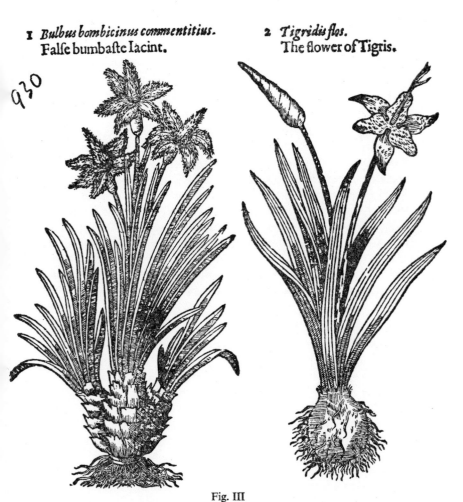

1 *Bulbus bombicinus commentitius.*
Falſe bumbaſte Iacint.

2 *Tigridis flos.*
The flower of Tigris.

930

Fig. III

Figures of two exotic plants sent by Rembert Dodoens to John Gerard.   No. 1:
the "false *bumbaste Iacint*" is, perhaps, a species of Hypoxis.   No. 2: "the
flower of Tigris" is *Tigridia pavonia, L.*

tum et radicum, Convolvulorum ae deletiarum Herbarum historiae libri III . . . Accessit appendix variarii . . . Stirpium, ac Florum quorundam peregrinosum", which had appeared at Antwerp in 1574. The fourth part was entitled: *"De Frumentis Leguminibus Palustribus et Acquatibibus . . . herbis"*, and like the two preceding parts was based on an earlier work by the author entitled *"Frumentorum, leguminum, palustrium, et aquatilium herbarum . . . historia"*, published at Antwerp in 1566, of which a second edition appeared there, with a slightly different title, in 1569. The fifth part was concerned with edible plants, and the sixth and last part with deciduous and evergreen trees and fruit-trees.

Though Dodoens classification was based upon the economic uses of plants, yet it brought together the members of some families of flowering plants, and effected a grouping of some genera. The book, and a review of Dodoens' botanical work is given, in some detail, in the biographical account of him in *Biographie Nationale de Belgique*, Vol. 6, (Bruxelles, 1878), Cols. 85–112. Few people were mentioned in the text, and such as were referred to, were either authors of earlier works, or owners of gardens. Each chapter began with a description of the plant, followed by an account of its habitat, time of flowering, and synonymy, after which was a discussion of, or remarks and observations on its medicinal or economic value.

Gerard corresponded with Dodoens, who, during his service in Vienna, between 1574 and 1580, sent a letter to Gerard, referring to Professor Johannes Aicholtz, of Vienna, whose name appeared in the list of authors cited in Dodoens' book of 1583. The letter enclosed the figures of two exotic plants, neither of which had appeared in Dodoens' book of 1583. At a later date, Gerard reproduced the two figures, referring to the letter and to Aicholtz. The fullest credit was thereby given to Dodoens, who did not long survive the publication of his book. He had removed from Malines to Leyden, where he died on 10th March, 1585. A memorial inscription was placed in St. Peter's Church, Leyden and a statue to his memory in the Botanic Garden at Malines.

In the year before Dodoens died, and L'Obel returned to London, Robert Priest, M.A., M.D., completed his studies at Cambridge and came down to London, where he married Katherine Boyce, on 27th April, 1584, at St. Peter's, Cornhill. This introduces Dr. Robert Priest, who subsequently translated some portion of the *Stirpium Historia Pemtades Sex* of Dodoens. One knows not when he began his translation work, but it seems likely that it was after

28

April, 1584. As a young, newly qualified and newly married physician, Dr. Priest had need to establish himself in practice, to which end he was admitted a Candidate of the College of Physicians, a status indicating his eligibility for consideration for election as a Fellow of the College when a vacancy occurred among existing Fellows. In 1581, the College had initiated a project for drawing up an antidotary, or pharmacopoeia, which seems to have been making only slow progress in 1584. With this project Dr. Priest later became associated.

Posthumous accounts of Dr. Priest's translation work, stated that he was requested to undertake it by Messrs. Bonham and John Norton, printers and booksellers of St. Paul's Churchyard, and that the expenses of it were defrayed by John Norton. Clearly such an approach could not have been made until April 1584, or soon afterwards. So when L'Obel returned to London in 1585, Dr. Priest had only just begun his task.

It is difficult to reconstruct the circumstances under which collaboration between Gerard and L'Obel was resumed in 1585, due to one's lack of knowledge of L'Obel's own activities between 1585 and 1596. By 1598, he had attracted the attention of Edward, Lord Zouche, who travelled on the Continent and in the Middle East from 1587 until 1593, spending some time in Constantinople. Upon his return he sent seeds of Middle Eastern plants to Gerard for his garden. When Lord Zouche was sent on a mission to Denmark in 1598, L'Obel was among those who accompanied him, and upon his return, Lord Zouche is said to have appointed L'Obel as superintendent of his garden at Hackney, Middlesex. If this is the correct date of that appointment, then L'Obel could have collaborated freely with Gerard from 1585 until 1597. It is certain that L'Obel made no addition to his printed works between 1581 and 1605.

The colonisation of Virginia in 1585 was an enterprise in which Sir Walter Raleigh was concerned, and in which JohnWhite played an important part. John White had been admitted a Freeman of the Painter-Stainers' Company of London in 1580, and took part in the voyage of reconnaissance in 1584, prior to the colonisation in 1585. He may have acted as an artist-recorder during the voyage; he certainly did so during the first colonising expedition in 1585–1586. He served as Governor of the "Cittie of Ralegh in Virginea" in 1587, returning the same year to England to secure supplies for the colonists. Preparations against the anticipated Spanish Armada made attempts to relieve the colony impracticable in 1588. In consequence the final effort to afford relief was not made until 1590, on which occasion, despite persistent efforts to do so, White failed to locate the colonists. He returned, therefore, to England, and was living at his home in Newtown, Kilmore, Ireland, on 4th February, 1593, after which date nothing is known of him. Gerard's meeting with him must have taken place on one of those occasions between 1584 and 1593 when John White was in London.

A decision in 1585 to support the cause of independence for which the Northern Provinces of the Netherlands were still struggling led to the despatch to Holland of an armed force under the command of Robert Dudley, Earl of Leicester. It embarked at Harwich, and two friends of Gerard's sailed with it as surgeons to the forces, namely William Gooderons and William Clowes. At this time, both men were members of the Company of Barber-Surgeons, the name of the senior man, William Gooderons, being spelt variously as Goderuns and Goodrowse in contemporary documents and printed works, but the spelling Gooderons used in this book is that employed when he made his Will. The military expedition proved abortive, and the Earl and his army were eventually withdrawn to England, but it had afforded useful experience to the two surgeons.

Upon their return, William Clowes took service in the Navy, but William Gooderons settled in London, and practised his profession there. Since 1581 the College of Physicians of London had been considering the possibility of preparing an antidotary or pharmacopoeia, and in 1586 it decided to establish a physic garden, selecting John Gerard to be its curator. Seemingly this garden was attached to the College buildings then situated in Knightrider Street, the premises having been formerly the home of Thomas Linacre, M.D. the Founder of the College. Gerard seems to have retained this post until 1603 or 1604. When this move came to the notice of the apothecaries of London it caused immediate concern.

Since 1378, the apothecaries had been incorporated in the Grocers' Company, having been previously a separate body. By 1586 they were becoming dissatisfied with this position, such that some apothecaries were beginning to seek disenfranchisement from the Company, and re-incorporation as a separate body. The custom, at this time, was for the physician to diagnose the illness and prescribe the remedy, and for the apothecary to dispense the prescription, and attend the patient. The medicaments used were mainly from plants, with some animal and mineral ingredients, but

1 Pulegium regium.
Pennie royall.

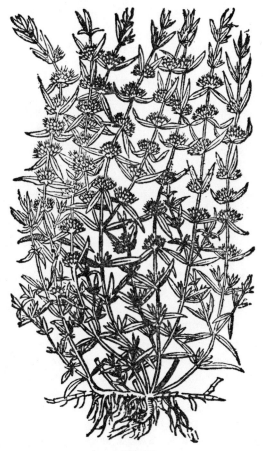

Fig. IV

Pulegium regium: "Pennie royall", grew, in Gerard's time at Mile End near London, "from whence poore women bring plentie to sell in London markets". (JOHN GERARD. *The Herball* (1597) p. 545.)

the basis of medicines was essentially herbal, so that the training of an apothecary during his period of apprenticeship obliged him to become practically acquainted with medicinal plants, as well as those in cultivation and those growing wild, which were studied during organised herborisations, or simplings, by groups of apothecaries and their apprentices. Such a practical knowledge was all the more essential since apothecaries depended, to some extent, for a supply of the medicinal plants they needed upon herb-gatherers, many of whom were women, who also retailed herbs in the open market.

Gerard subsequently referred to them, and herb-women remained active well into the eighteenth century. The proposal of the College of Physicians to establish a physic garden was regarded, in consequence, by the apothecaries as an encroachment upon their own profession, and was a factor that intensified their desire for separate incorporation. In 1588 moves were made, designed to attain that end, but during Gerard's lifetime the apothecaries were unsuccessful in achieving it.

Having been elected Third Warden of the Barber-Surgeons' Company in 1583, Richard Sprignell was elected its Master in August 1586. In the same year, a second edition appeared of Henry Lyte's book as *A New Herbal, London* (N. Newton), 1586, and a third edition was published in London in 1595, being the last to appear during Lyte's lifetime.

For the year 1587–1588, the office of Master of the Barber-Surgeons' Company was filled by the election thereto of William Gooderons, who thereby occupied it during the critical period when the Spanish Armada appeared in the English Channel.

That period of tension being over, the College of Physicians decided to intensify its efforts to produce a pharmacopoeia, to which end a comitia was set up on 10th October, 1589, which was entusted with the task of preparing one. The Comitia was subdivided into eleven sections, of which Section I was composed of Dr. Edward Atslowe, Lancelot Browne, John Farmery and Robert Priest, who were to draw up formulae for Syrups, Juleps and Decoctions. The section ran into difficulties almost immediately, as John Farmery died, and was buried on 21st March, 1589–90, which must have affected the translation work upon which Dr. Priest was perhaps still engaged. The personnel of this section were men of particular ability and importance in the history of Elizabethan medicine.

The entries in the London Subsidy Roll for 1589 are relevant at this point. Dr. Edward Atslowe, a member of Section I, is shown therein as a resident of Cripplegate Ward, and subsequently he had property at Downham, Essex. Gerard, however, had close relations with other men listed in the Roll. The first was Hugh Morgan, the apothecary and the second was William De Laune, M.D., both of whom were known to Pena and L'Obel in 1570. William De Laune, at that time was a French Protestant refugee in London, and practised medicine without license for some years, but was eventually licensed so to practice by the College of Physicians on 22nd November, 1582. Pena and L'Obel, in their *Stirpium Adversaria Nova* recorded that William De Laune showed them a specimen of *Nux peregrina Indica*. Another friend of Gerard was Timothy Bright, M.D., who was shown in the Roll as a physician in the Parish of St. Bartholomew-the-Less, and was also the inventor of shorthand, while William Gooderons, was recorded as a resident in the Parish of St. Andrew, Holborn, where, apparently, he had settled in practice as a surgeon upon his return from Holland. Thereby he became a near neighbour of Gerard, and one of his closest friends. All these men lived and worked in the western part of the City of London, but the Roll included the names of two friends of Gerard in the eastern portion of the City. They were Thomas Gray, apothecary, and James Cole, merchant, both of them resident in the Parish of St. Dionys Back-church.

In Germany, Jacob Theodor Dietrich, of Bergzabern, published the first volume of his *Kreuterbuch*, at Frankfurt-am-Main in 1589, a work illustrated by woodcuts, and the blocks were used to illustrate his *Eicones*, issued at the same place in 1590, as an oblong-octavo book, containing only the plant names and the figures. There was no text. The author died in 1590, leaving the second volume of his *Kreuterbuch* to appear posthumously in 1591. His contemporaries knew him better as *Tabernaemontanus*, as, in accordance with a customary practice, he so Latinised the name of his place of residence. Gerard, not surprisingly, referred to him by that name, but in this book he will be called Bergzabern.

The eminent French surgeon, Ambroise Paré, died in 1590. Though distinguished as a surgeon generally, he became especially notable as a military surgeon in consequence of his successful treatment of gunshot-wounds. This topic had formed the subject of a book by the English surgeon, Thomas Gale, which was followed by a treatise upon the same matter by Ambroise Paré. Subsequently, William Gooderons and William Clowes had practical experience in treating gunshot wounds during their service in Holland in 1585, the results of which William Clowes embodied in a book in 1588, published that year in London under the title *Prooved Practise for All Young Chirurgions*, wherein, in addition to an account of the expedition of 1585, Clowes observed that Gooderons and he lost no cases from gunshot wounds, save those mortally wounded at once. Gerard's own interest in gunshot wounds was evidenced, at a later time, by his reference to the subject in *The Herball* in 1597, and it is thus traceable to his friendship with these two experienced men. Clowes, in his books, referred approvingly to Gerard.

At some time before 1590, Gerard collected plants at Barnes, Surrey near the home of Sir Francis Walsingham, Kt., who died there in that year, while, in London, Thomas Gray, apothecary, of Lime Street, also passed away, leaving behind him the garden with which Gerard had been acquainted. At the time of his death, Sir Francis Walsingham was Secretary of State, a post he had held until 1573, before which he had been Ambassador resident in Paris from 1570 until 1573. About 1567 he had married, as his second wife, Lady (Ursula) Worsley, widow of Sir Richard Worsley, of Upchurch, and during his tenure of his post in Paris, he met Robert Beale, a Marian exile, who had been connected with the English embassy there since 1564. During Walsingham's period of office as Ambassador, Robert Beale became his secretary, and the two men remained closely associated until Walsingham's death in 1590. They also became brothers-in-law, as Robert Beale married Edith St. Barbe, sister of Lady (Ursula) Walsingham. At the time he served as Ambassador in Paris, Walsingham's home was at Foots Cray, Kent, but having been knighted in 1577, he removed in 1579 to Barnes, Surrey, so Gerard's visit there was made between 1579 and 1590. Nor was he the only botanist to collect plants in that area. Robert Beale presumably returned to England with Walsingham in 1573, as he was Clerk to Her Majesty's Council from about 1573 until 1591. He too resided at Barnes, and in a close next to his house *Veronica spicata L.* was to be found growing. Gerard's friend, Stephen Bredwell, found it in that spot, during an excursion to Barnes, made independently of that of Gerard, so far as can be judged.

In 1590, Gerard made an excursion to Hampstead in search of plants, during which he met Sir John Hart, who was then serving his year of office as Lord Mayor of London, during which he received the honour of Knighthood before 12th March, 1590. As Gerard referred to him as Sir John Hart, the meeting took place after that date, at which time Sir John Hart's influence in the affairs of the

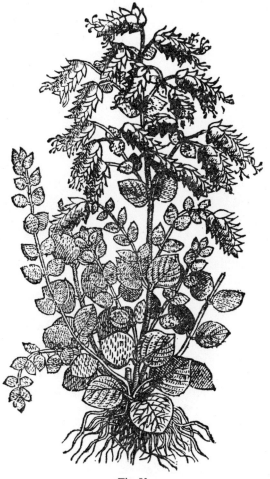

1 *Dictamnum Creticum.*
Dittanie of Candie.

Fig. V

Dictamnum creticum: "Dittanie of Candie", a native of Crete. Grown by
Gerard in his garden from seed, but killed during an extraordinarily cold winter.
(JOHN GERARD. *The Herball* (1597) p. 651.)
Used in the care of gunshot wounds.

City of London was rising. For some years he had been an active member of the Common Council, and was already an Alderman in 1590. At the time of his meeting with Gerard he was interested in a project for conveying water to London from the Springs at Hampstead. It was there that the meeting took place. In 1591, Sir John Hart was Governor of the Russia Company, whose members traded to the Baltic and Russia, and, in 1593, he was President of St. Bartholomew's Hospital, London, and retained that office until his death in 1604. He was Surveyor-General of Hospitals from 1594 until 1602, and Controller-General of Hospitals from 1602 until 1604. He was one of the chief founders of the East India Company in 1600. It is clear that Sir John Hart was closely associated with the health services and with the medical men of London from 1593 onwards, if not earlier.

At the annual elections in 1591, Richard Wood became Master of the Company of Barber-Surgeons. He was probably the surgeon of that name afterwards recorded as practising in Ratcliff, Stepney, Middlesex, where his patients included seamen, some of whom referred to him in their Wills. Richard Sprignell was elected First Warden; George Baker as Second Warden and James Bates as Third Warden. The Company's Hall in Monkwell Street was commonly called Surgeon's Hall, and situated in the Ward of Farringdon Within, just inside the City walls. Adjoining this ward to the west, and outside the walls, was the parish of St. Sepulchre wherein George Baker resided and practised his profession. The Fleet River separated this parish from that of St. Andrew, Holborn, further to the west, and it was then open and navigable as far as the stone structure known as Holborn Bridge, which linked the two parishes. Clearly George Baker was within easy distance of the Company's Hall, and equally within easy reach of Gerard's home and garden in Holborn. Gerard's home was on the south side of Holborn, at its junction with Fetter Lane. Westwards of it were several Inns of Court, as far as Staple Inn and Holborn Bar. Just beyond the Bar, on the north side of the street was Gray's Inn, one of whose members, Edmund Cartwright, was a patient of Gerard between 1578 and 1597, having received a severe wound reaching to the lungs, for which he was treated successfully. Gerard's remedial measures, included the use of Clown's Woundwort, of whose curative properties he had learned from a reaper during one of his excursions into Kent.

Though George Baker and William Clowes had a strong difference of opinion about 1577, whatever the subsequent nature of their

36

mutual relations was, both men remained friends of Gerard. Elizabethan surgeons have been described as noisy, self-opinionated and quarrelsome, but this was by no means confined to surgeons, so that no undue importance should be attached to their reported differences of view.

George Baker descended from a Kentish family, whose entitlement to bear a shield of arms and crest was confirmed on 10th May, 1573, and William Clowes received a grant of arms in 1576. Two other friends of Gerard received similar grants, Richard Garth, who had purchased the manor at Morden, Surrey, in 1553, had received a grant of arms in 1564, while Gerard was yet an apprentice-surgeon. Richard Garth succeeded his father, as one of the six Clerks of the Petty Bag in the Court of Chancery, an appointment he held until his death in 1598. In that capacity he had the use of a house set apart for the use of the six Clerks, which was situated in Chancery Lane, west of Clifford's Inn in Fleet Street. This would place it at the southern end of Chancery Lane, on the east side, within the Ward of Farringdon Without in the Parish of St. Dunstan's-in-the-West, Fleet Street.

When Richard Garth made his Will he was described therein as of this parish, but expressed a wish to be buried in Morden, Surrey. Gerard collected plants on land called Groutes, near Croydon, Surrey, which Richard Garth owned, and Garth's residence, when on duty, in the house of the six Clerks, made him a comparatively near neighbour of Gerard. It is worth notice that when John Stow was writing his book *A Survey of London*, written in the year 1598, he mentioned this house in Chancery Lane, which he described as reserved for the five Clerks of the Court of Chancery, so that, although Stow does not mention Richard Garth, it is clear that he wrote his account of the Ward of Farringdon Without after Garth's death. Gerard almost certainly knew this house well, because turning west out of his house in Holborn, and passing Holborn Bar, a few steps would have brought him to the nothern end of Chancery Lane, at which point, on the east side of the Lane, opposite Gray's Inn, was a walled property enclosing the houses and grounds of Southampton House, the residence of the Earl of Southampton. In later years, Gerard recorded a plant he found growing on the wall of this property. Turning down Chancery Lane he would have passed the house of the six Clerks, and reaching Fleet Street, in a few steps westwards, he would have entered the Strand, and so to Lord Burghley's London residence and garden. Finally, a grant of arms was made to Hugh Morgan in 1588, he being then Apothecary to Queen Elizabeth.

There were two other events of 1591 needing notice. On the 1st December of that year a commission was granted to Henry Cavendish and six others, and to the escheator of Derbyshire, to inquire after the death of Sir Thomas Fitzherbert, to whom Gerard referred at a later time, the object of which was to prepare an Inquisition Post Mortem—an inventory of his household goods.

The other event was the re-publication of William Clowes' book *A Prooved Practise for All Young Chirurgions*, which was "Newly corrected and augmented", and "Printed by Thomas Orwyn for Wydlow Broome, 1591"—a small slim volume printed, as to the title page and medicinal recipes in Roman type, and otherwise in black-letter. The text was prefaced by a commendation from the distinguished surgeon, John Banister. The pages were without numbers, but they record details from William Clowes' surgical practises, and record the medicinal recipes he employed, wherein plant products figure almost exclusively, and show clearly the importance they then occupied in surgical healing work. There are references to contemporary surgeons, and the plants in the medicinal recipes are all readily identifiable. The reason for this appeared when Clowes described a drink, to which his attention had been directed, called Potus Antiochiae, which he employed successfully. It was an ancient medicine, but had been used in London for the first time by Mr. Archenbole, and made by him, Mr. Gates and other surgeons. It was prepared from twenty medicinal plants, and was a remedy for wounds, especially sword wounds. Of recipes for compounding this drink Clowes "had divers ancient copies, but none so true as those which Maister Thorn(e)y, did friendly send me, and also Maister Iaret (Gerard) who hath been very willing to shewe me his booke wherein this drinke was also described, and moreover hath readily assisted me to give every hearb his true and proper name, which was somewhat obscure in the ancient copies, as hath also shewed and found out the hearbes themselves each one in his time and kind: which drink (as my author sayth) must be finished and made before Midsomer." Here is a first-hand, valuable contemporary reference to Gerard's botanical work by one who was not only a friend, but an eminent surgeon of his day. The copy of this instructive little book in the British Museum is in nineteenth century boards, and contains some manuscript notes.

On 4th February, 1592, William Gooderons was appointed Serjeant Surgeon to Queen Elizabeth, at a fee of forty marks a year, and on the same day, George Baker was appointed one of Her Majesty's Surgeons. On the 5th February, 1592, there was a liberate on the patent to Gooderons, and another to Baker for the payment of forty pounds a year.

In August 1593, Gooderons became First Warden of the Barber-Surgeons Company, and was Master in 1594, when John Iszard became Second Warden. The reference by William Clowes to Thomas Thorney and John Gerard is relevant to the fact that Thorney, Gerard and Gooderons were all residents in the parish of St. Andrew, Holborn, and carried on their respective practices there. Gooderons had an even closer link with Gerard as he shared with him a taste for horticulture. The earliest reference by Gerard himself to his garden was in 1579; during the winter of 1579–1580 he suffered the loss of some plants. This date is very close to 1577, when he entered the service of Lord Burghley, which again suggests that Gerard was settled in Holborn, and had a garden there by 1577.

At Mortlake, Surrey, Francis Dee, a son of John Dee, M.A., mathematician and astrologer, fell ill in the summer of 1594. The illness was short and Francis quickly succumbed to it. John Dee was also seized with an indisposition, and on 12th August, 1594, he received a visit from John Gerard. The inference is that the visit was almost certainly a professional one, since on an earlier occasion, Queen Elizabeth had manifested concern when Dee fell ill, comforts having been sent to him from Whitehall. It is possible that Gerard's visit was a reflection of the Queen's continued interest in Dee's welfare, since one of her Serjeant Surgeons, William Gooderons, was one of Gerard's friends.

When the annual election of the Barber-Surgeons' Company was held in 1595, William Gale was elected Master, James Bates filled the office of Second Warden, and John Gerard was elected to the Court of Assistants. In the same year he submitted to the court a scheme for a garden for medicinal plants, and suggested that land belonging to the Company at East Smithfield, near the Tower of London, might be used for this purpose, but some members of the Court considered the proposed site unsuitable. One may infer from this that the garden of the College of Physicians was not developing to Gerard's satisfaction, and the area available for it in Knightrider Street could not have been large. The objection to East Smithfield as a site for the garden probably arose from its situation. In 1596, it was an open space, in the Tower precinct, just outside the walls of the City, and occupied an area lying to the north and north-east of the Tower of London. A few buildings had been erected upon it, and it was feared that, perhaps, further building might take place, as indeed it did, as the area developed rapidly as a residential one. Gerard was certainly familiar with this part of London as he had a firend living nearby in the Parish of St. Botolph in the Minories, to the east of the Tower. This was Thomas Goodman, who was recorded as resident there in the London Subsidy Roll in 1589, and he retained property there until his death in 1607 at West Ham, Essex. The provision of a garden came forward again on 26th March, 1596, on a motion of Messrs. Fettiplace, John Laycock and John Gerard concerning the demissing of certain garden grounds at East Smithfield for which they were suitors. It was agreed that the ground should be let for a yearly rent at the pleasure of the Masters or Governors of the Company, and none of the three suitors received any grant of land. But, inasmuch as John Gerard's request was to use it for the furtherance of learning in the knowledge and practice of the nature and skill of herbs, it was thought not a place fit for that purpose, so that a more convenient place should be sought for, and divers of the Company offered to be contributors for the buying of land. Messrs. Fettiplace and John Laycock were to be spoken with and thus satisfied, but the next reference to the garden did not occur until over twelve months later.

In pressing the Company to provide a physic garden, Gerard was not acting in any way prejudicial to that of the College of Physicians in Knightrider Street, for which he was already responsible. He may have had in mind the fact that, at that time, herbs were used in the course of their professional work by physicians, apothecaries and surgeons alike, and reference will be made, later, to Gerard's efforts to instruct his colleagues in a knowledge of herbs, which he carried out of his own accord. It shows clearly his desire and active attempts to raise the professional standards in his profession, both in regard to knowledge and practice.

Meanwhile, Gerard's attention turned to his own garden, and in 1596, he issued the first of two catalogues of its contents, as "*Catalogus arborum, fruticum, ac plantarum tam indigenarum, quam exoticarum, in horto Johannis Gerardi, civis et Chirurgi Londinensis nascentium*". Beneath this title was the Royal Arms in a garter, and below that the colophon read: "*Londoni, Ex officina Roberti Robinson, 1596*". This was a quarto catalogue, dedicated to Lord

Burghley, the dedication being in Latin. At the end was an attestation, written in Latin by Matthias de L'Obel, that he had seen Gerard's garden, and that Gerard had grown all the plants named in the catalogue. L'Obel signed it, and added the date: "June, 1596". From the appearance of the original catalogue in the British Museum, Dr. B. Daydon Jackson was led to infer that this issue was intended for private circulation only.

The identity of the printer is not easy to determine, but he was, perhaps, Robert Robinson, who died intestate in the Parish of St. Andrew, Holborn, letters of administration in respect of his estate being granted in June, 1607. The catalogue was an historic production, as it was the first printed list of the contents of a garden in England to be published. Very many years later, William Aiton, Gardener to Kew House, Surrey had access to a copy of this catalogue, which enabled him to insert in his "*Hortus Kewensis*" (London, 1789) the dates at which many exotic plants were known to have been first cultivated in England. These dates have been assumed to represent the date of introduction of the plants concerned, but this is a misapprehension. Another event of 1596 was a proposal by Gerard to Lord Burghley that he should be recommended for appointment as Herbarist at the University of Cambridge. It took the form of a letter, written by Gerard in Latin, with a request for Lord Burghley's signature to it if he approved the proposal. This is preserved in the British Museum (Lansdowne MSS, 107, No. 92, Fol. 155). Though the suggestion was not approved, one should note that Gerard's circle of friends included a number of Cambridge men, among whom were John Marsh, M.D., who practised medicine in Cambridge, Nicholas Belson (c. 1535–1591), schoolmaster in Suffolk, and the Rev. George Fuller, (1561–1591), whom he visited at his Rectory at Hildersham, Cambridgeshire, so that he was in Suffolk aud Cambridgeshire before 1591.

Writing in *The Herball* in 1597, Gerard recorded that early in that year he suffered a severe attack of ague, and on 20th April, 1597, his two friends, William Gooderons and George Baker, the Queen's Serjeant Surgeon and Surgeon, received a lease in reversion, without proviso for tenants, for forty years, of Nunnington mansion house, and divers lands, tenements and woods in Northfleet, Gravesend, Milton, etc. in the county of Kent, and in the counties of York, Norfolk, and Suffolk . . . and without fine in respect of their service to the Queen.

At a Court of the Company of Barber-Surgeons held on 16th June, 1597, the possibility of establishing a garden was again discussed, and at the request of John Peck, thirteen members of the Court were instructed to survey a piece of ground fit for making into a garden in which to plant "all kindes of herbs, roots, plants and such like, as Mr. Gerard, a skillful Herbalist, should think meet for the worship (i.e. credit) of the Company, and to report to the Court their opinion and actions therein, eight, ten or the most part of them to form a quorum". At the Annual Elections in August, 1597, George Baker was elected Master with John Iszard, as First Warden, Thomas Warren, as Second Warden, and John Gerard as Third Warden. Of these officers, Messrs. Iszard and Warren were among the thirteen members of the Court who had been instructed in June to investigate the possibility of securing land for a garden, and in the record of that meeting it is worth noticing the evident appreciation, by his professional colleagues, of Gerard's ability as a herbalist. His election to the office of Third Warden was a further mark of their good esteem. At this stage, the situation seems to have been particularly favourable for the eventual establishment of a physic garden. The Master, George Baker, a close friend of Gerard, had a personal acquaintance with Gerard's own garden, and John Iszard and Thomas Warren, the two senior Wardens were members of the Committee entrusted with securing a site for a physic garden, while some Members of the Court had already signified their willingness to support the scheme financially.

For his part, Gerard, at this time, was fully occupied in completing a task which had employed him for some years previously. On 6th June, 1597, his book *The Herball*, or *Generall Historie of Plantes*, was entered at Stationers Hall, but he did not write his "Address to the Courteous, Well-Willing Reader", until 1st December, 1597, on which date he signed it at his house in the Parish of St. Andrew, Holborn. When the book was published it had an engraved copper-plate title-page, the title being set in a decorative border of figures, flowers and fruits, beneath which was an illustration of a garden of rectangular beds, such as was then favoured. The colophon announced the book was "Imprinted at London by John Norton, 1597". Then followed the dedication to Sir William Cecil, Lord Burghley, wherein Gerard referred to his twenty years' association with him in the supervision of his gardens. After that, in accordance with the custom of the time, appeared some commendations, in prose and verse, of the book and its author. There were

42

Anisum.
Anise.

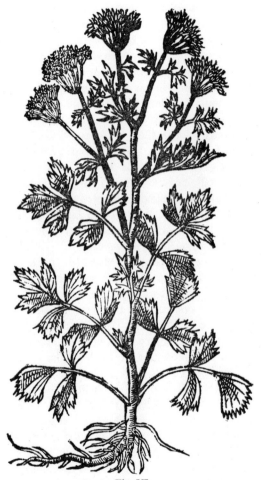

Fig. VI

Anisum: anise, a native of Crete, Syria, Egypt and other Middle Eastern countries. Grown by Gerard in his garden, where it "brought foorth his ripe seede", when the season permitted. (JOHN GERARD. *The Herball* (1597) p. 880.)

43

twelve such commendations, which appeared in the following sequence.

The first was in Latin, and dated December, 1597, from Lancelot Browne, M.A., M.D., F.C.P. Lond., (d. 1605), Physician to Queen Elizabeth, and father-in-law of William Harvey, M.D., afterwards distinguished for his discovery of the circulation of the blood. The contribution of the next contributor, Matthias de L'Obel, M.D. (1538–1616), physician and botanist, was in Latin and dated December, 1597. Then came a short Latin verse from Anthony Hunton, M.A., whom the University of Cambridge licensed to practise medicine in 1589, and on the same page were some Latin lines by G. Lannaeus, who was William De Laune, M.D., of the Ward of Farringdon Within, London, in 1589, and a French Protestant refugee there since 1582. He had met Pena and L'Obel in London, and they mentioned him in their book, so William De Laune had been resident in London since 1570. He married Catherine Loges, and was the father of Gideon de Laune, apothecary, afterwards prominent in the affairs of the Society of Apothecaries; of Isaac De Laune, whom Gerard called "a learned physician", and Paul De Laune, M.D., F.C.P. Lond., who died in Jamaica. The sixth contribution was a brief Latin epigram from James Johnston, of Edinburgh, "*Ballincrisae Regii pagi portionarii*", which was followed by a longer one by Francis Herring, M.A., (d. 1628), who graduated M.D. in 1597, the year of the publication of *The Herball*. He afterwards distinguished himself as a physician, and had an interest in botany. The eighth contributor, the Rev. Thomas Newton, was, like Gerard, a native of Cheshire. His contribution of some Latin lines, was headed in reference to Gerard, "*amico non vulgari*". Queen Elizabeth had presented Newton to the Rectory of Little Ilford, Essex, about 1583, and he had contributed a commendatory epigram to Henry Lyte's book in 1578, beside which he had published *An Herball for the Bible*, at London in 1587. The ninth contribution was in English verse and has apparently never been noticed by biographers of Gerard. It was written by one who knew him well, a fellow parishioner, and a fellow surgeon. This was Thomas Thorney, (1542-3—1614), who styled himself, as Gerard styled himself, "Master of Chirurgerie", Thomas Thorney addressed his verses to "his learned friend and loving brother in Art", and they testified to his personal knowledge of Gerard's life and character, to his love of plants, and his services to botany and his profession. The Rev. William Westerman, M.A., (*fl.* 1587–1622), the tenth contributor, was, in 1597, Vicar of Sandridge, Hertfordshire, where

44

he had been instituted on 11th February, 1594. He was afterward D.D., and preached a sermon at St. Albans before James I, during his progress in 1612. These facts lead one to infer that Gerard made his acquaintance during his visits to Theobalds. The eleventh contributor was Stephen Bredwell, L.C.P. Lond., physician, of whom more will be said presently. The twelfth and last contribution came from George Baker, Surgeon to Queen Elizabeth, and in 1597, Master of the Company of Barber-Surgeons of London. George Baker was born at Tenterden, Kent, and married Anne, the daughter of William Swanne, of Hawcke (Hook) Green, Southfleet, Kent, whom Gerard mentioned in *The Herball*. In one place he is called "William Swaine", Baker styled himself "Master of the Chirurgions of London", which implies that he held an office in the City of London, which the City authorities created in 1451, for the purpose of supervising the practices of surgeons within the liberties of the City, on order to ensure the maintenance of a good standard of professional conduct and service.

Altogether, *The Herball* was sponsored by friends of the author, who were then, or afterwards, distinguished in their respective fields of work. It is worth notice that four of them have found a place in the *Dictionary of National Biography*, namely Drs. Lancelot Browne, and Francis Herring, the Rev. Thomas Newton, and George Baker, surgeon. Biographical and bibliographical references to them, and to all the remaining contributors, except James Johnston, have been found in other standard reference works.

Following the commendations, was Gerard's address to the reader, and after that was the engraved copper-plate portrait of him by William Rogers, which was dated "*aetatis suae 1598*", which together with the dating of two of the commendations and of Gerard's address in December 1597, rather suggests that *The Herball* did not appear until early in 1598. The portrait depicted Gerard as holding a flowering spray of the potato plant, (*Solanum tuberosum, L.*) which he was the first person to grow in England. Beneath the portrait appeared the arms and crest of Gerard, namely Gerard of Ince, quartering Ince of Ince, a crescent for difference. At the bottom left; those of the City of London, (bottom centre); and those of the Company of Barber-Surgeons, (bottom right).

Stephen Bredwell's contribution was important but little is known of the man himself. A native of Oxford, he attended the University there, but, so far as is known, he came down without taking a degree, and migrated to London, where after having been twice examined by the College of Physicians, he received his License from that body on 2nd August, 1594, and was thereby able to practise medicine in London. Gerard's acquaintance with him probably dates from 1594, but Bredwell left London soon afterwards and was practising as a physician in Wiltshire in 1597. Under the initials "S.B.", two theological tracts had appeared in London in 1586 and 1588, and each was the work of Stephen Bredwell, but one of them, on examination, disclosed no connection with the physician, who settled near Chippenham in Wiltshire. In *The Herball*, Gerard referred to a journey he made to Bristol, and the west of England, during which he passed through Chippenham, and mentioned Bredwell as being in practice in the vicinity. Alone of the commendors of *The Herball*, Stephen Bredwell seemingly had personal knowledge of Dr. Priest's translation work, and had at least a rough idea of the stage it had reached. According to Bredwell, Dr. Priest left his translation unfinished at his death, a fact which Gerard confirmed, while his own reference to Dr. Priest placed his death as having occurred between late in 1596 and before 1st December, 1597. Bredwell's reference to Dr. Priest's translation was in the following terms:

"The first gatherers out of the Ancients and augmentors, by their owne paines have already spread the odour of their good names throughout all the lands of learned habitations. D. Priest, for his translations of so much of Dodonaeus hath thereby left a tombe for his honourable sepulture."

This seems to mean that Dr. Priest had translated perhaps the greater part of the *Stirpium Historia Pemptades Sex*, of Dodoens, but died before he could finish it. Dr. Agnes Arber so interpreted this passage and her conclusion concerning it seems correct. Bredwell continued:

"M. Gerard coming last, but not the least, hath many ways accommodated the whole work to our English Nation: for this History of Plants as it is richly replenished by those five men's labours laid together, so yet could it full ill have wanted that new accession he has made unto it."

A marginal entry names the five men referred to: Dr. William Turner, Dr. Pierre Pena, Dr. Matthias de L'Obel, Dr. Rembert Dodoens and Jakob Theodor Bergzabern. Each of these authors is specifically referred to by Gerard in his text. Bredwell here confirms the impression gained from an examination of Gerard's text that the publications of these men were the main sources of the material in *The Herball*. To these one may add the writings of Pliny, whom Gerard often quoted, and the *Niewe Herball*, of Henry Lyte. The early works of Charles de L'Escluse may be included. Bredwell's remarks clearly indicate that Gerard collated the works of Dr. William Turner; the *Stirpium Adversaria Nova*, of Pena and L'Obel;

the *Stirpium Historiae Pemptades Sex*, of Dodoens, and the *Kreuter-buch*, of Bergzabern, supplementing it with material from other sources, and from personal observations, or material supplied by friends and correspondents. Gerard's text confirms it.

One may note here that among very recent authors, Gerard utilised the publications of Jacques D'Alechamps and Joachim Camerarius the Younger.

George Baker's commendatory letter included these remarks:

"I protest upon my conscience, I do not think for the knowledge of Plants, that he (Gerard) is inferior to any; for I did once see him tried with one of the best strangers that ever came into England, by that famous man, Ambrose Parè; and he being here was desirous to go abroad with some of our Herbarists; for the which I was the means to bring them together, and one whole day was spent therein searching the rarest simples, but when it came to the triall, my Frenchman did not know one to his four."

Baker's letter shows that he was personally acquainted with the contents of Gerard's garden, which had been assembled "at his proper cost and charges", to which Thomas Thorney also bore witness. Baker contrasted the cases of Gerard and Mattioli:

"What age do we live in here that will suffer all vertue to go unrewarded ? Master Gerard hath taken more pains than ever Matthiolus did in his Commentaries (on Dioscorides), and has corrected a number of faults that he passed over, and I dare affirm that Master Gerard doth know a greater number of simples that were not known in his time; and yet I doubt whether he shall taste of the liberality of either Prince, Duke, Earl, Bishop or public Estate."

After the commendations, Gerard's address to the reader, and his portrait there followed the text of *The Herball*, which occupied 1,392 pages, illustrated by woodcuts, the great majority of which were imported from Frankfurt-am-Main by John Norton, after they had been used to illustrate the *Eicones*, of Jakob Theodor Bergzabern in 1590. There were sixteen cuts which did not appear in that work, nor did Gerard follow the same sequence as the figures occupied in that book. This was partly due to his having followed L'Obel in the first part of *The Herball*, and partly to his having placed some of Bergzabern's figures under genera to which they more properly belonged. A very few seem to have been omitted altogether. Of the cuts not provided by John Norton, two were provided by L'Obel, two by Dodoens, and two others were reproduced from the *Stirpium Adversaria Nova* of Pena and L'Obel. Gerard apparently supplied the remainder.

The two figures from the *Stirpium Adversaria Nova* (1570–1571) are of cacti, and deserve a little notice. They occur in that work on pages 452 and 453, and both kinds were supplied to Gerard for his garden by his friend, William Martin, whom he called "a right expert surgeon"; William Martin had obtained the plants from North Africa, whence he had sent his servant as a ship's surgeon. The first plant Gerard called *Cereus peruvianus spinosus L'Obelii*, a name to be found in the *Stirpium Adversaria Nova*, on page 453, but the second plant was figured therein on page 452 as *Palmacea aut Arundinacea pinnata spinosa*, whereas Gerard named it (*Herball*, p.1015) *Cereus peruvianus spinosus L'Obelii*.

Gerard arranged his text in three Books: Book I, pp. 1–176; Book II, pp. 177–1076, and Book III, pp. 1077–1392. Each book was preceded by a Proeme, and each book sub-divided into Chapters. It will be noticed that the first book is the smallest, and this is the one in which the influence of L'Obel is most evident, but a comparison of the *Stirpium Adversaria Nova* with this Book shows no close agreement with it, as Gerard quickly introduced into his text material which does not figure in the book of Pena and L'Obel. The small size of this first book, its evident close association with L'Obel, and some biographical details derivable from it suggest that an early manuscript of it existed between 1569 and 1574. The *Stirpium Adversaria Nova* is frequently cited throughout *The Herball*, and its authors referred to appreciatively. The method of citation was not consistent. On some occasions it was referred to as by Pena, the senior author, only, and inquiry shows that contemporary authors followed this method. On other occasions both authors were cited. There was at least one case (*Herball*, pp. 716–717), when Gerard seemed to quote from an earlier work by Pena only, written and published about 1561 or 1562. Gerard was discussing *Scammonium syriacum*, (*Convolvulus scammonia L.*) and its valuable properties, mentioning that false scammonies were passed off as the real thing, and added "by reason of the counterfeiting and ill-mixing thereof, I have thought good to set downe what I have taken out of the diligent and no lesse learned observations of Pena concerning this plant, *Anno* 1561 or 1562". In the next paragraph Gerard referred to Martinelli, an apothecary of Venice, who visited Antioch, and sent seeds to Padua, and later to Antwerp, where among others, William Dries, apothecary, grew it in his garden. Gerard referred his readers to Pena for its proper uses.

In point of fact Gerard evidently made a slip in his dates, which should read, 1571, because Pena and L'Obel described this plant in the *Stirpium Adversaria Nova* (pp. 273–274), where they mentioned

Alberto Martinelli sent seends from Aleppo to Venice and Padua, and afterwards to William Dries, of Antwerp, who was also a correspondent of L'Obel. Here then Gerard was quoting from the *Stirpium Adversaria Nova*, of Pena and L'Obel when he seems to have been writing from memory. Hence the discrepancy in the date.

The relationship of *The Herball* to Dodoens' *Stirpium Historiae Pemptades Sex*, (1583), has been much discussed, but the view that the first of these two books is a translation of the second, with the material rearranged to conform to L'Obel's scheme of plant classification is difficult to accept. A comparison of the two books shows that Dodoens' closely adhered to a scheme of classification, essentially pharmacological in character, and the plants described were almost entirely those then held to possess medicinal properties. Gerard, on the other hand, was writing for a very different audience, and a wider one, beside which he aimed to include medicinal, culinary and economic plants, as well as indigenous and exotic plants that did not fall within any of those categories. Hence Dodoens' classification would not have answered his purpose fully. Moreover he had already started to base his work on the classification of L'Obel before Dodoens' last book appeared in 1583. These factors seem to explain why Gerard did not follow Dodoens' classification, and that he did not throw over that classification since he was already using another more botanical one.

Gerard's book cannot be regarded, in consequence, as a direct translation from any previous work, but from its nature, it owed much to the works of earlier authors. Though Gerard did not provide a list of authors consulted, a study of his pages shows very frequent acknowledgment to earlier as well as to contemporary writers, but in such a massive work it was inevitable that, from time to time, there should be omissions of acknowledgments, especially if, as suggested here, the book was prepared at different times over a period of years. In those circumstances it would be unwise to infer that Gerard intended any discourtesy to other authors.

Gerard was capable of translating from Latin authors such passages as he wished to use. When he said he was no scholar nor a graduate, one should remember that the training then available to those intending to enter upon surgery as a career was such as to prevent the majority of surgeons becoming proficient in Greek, and the limiting effect upon the syllabus of apprentice-surgeons exerted by the College of Physicians. With that body Gerard was apparently on good terms, and he was courteous to, and appreciative of the

College in referring to it in his book. Had it been otherwise, the College would scarcely have selected him to be the Curator of their proposed physic garden.

George Baker's commendation of Gerard showed clearly that he was considered to possess an excellent knowledge of the flora of England, which is confirmed by an examination of his text. He was an excellent field botanist, but made no pretension to being a taxonomist, though he did have some ability as such. His localities are instructive, and in cases, not very many in so large a work, where the plant has not since been found, the reason for it is susceptible of explanation. So far as they have been examined, no fault has been found with them, and this again should contribute to confidence in the author's integrity.

If the London area is regarded as a distinct locality, then Gerard collected plants in fourteen areas in England, which for the most part, form natural groups. The areas most commonly visited were those easily accessible in and around London, but others needed more extensive journeys to reach. The county boundaries being then very different, and London a smaller place, Gerard had readily accessible as plant habitats localities in Kent, Surrey and Middlesex, but he made longer excursions into Kent, East Sussex, Hampshire, Hertfordshire and Essex. There was a journey westwards into Wiltshire and Somersetshire, and another, roughly north-eastern, through Essex to Cambridgeshire. Of the two northern journeys it is difficult to ascertain the routes taken, but the areas visited were Cheshire and Lancashire, on the one hand, and Nottinghamshire, and the West Riding of Yorkshire, on the other. Finally there is a reference to a fragment of a journey to south-east Surrey, and the adjoining area in Sussex, which cannot be linked to any other journey.

Gerard's plant collections sometimes occurred when he was carrying out a professional visit in the areas outside London, which brought him into contact with other medical men. Such was the case with John Bennett, surgeon, of Maidstone, and that may apply when Gerard met Robert Cranwise the Younger, surgeon of Great Dunmow, and Thomas Buxton, apothecary, of Colchester. Possibly also with Nicholas Swayton, of Faversham. Other journeys on behalf of Lord Burghley led to Gerard's acquaintance with the Rev. Robert Abbot, of Hatfield, Hertfordshire, and with the Rev. William Westerman, of Sandridge, in the same county. Still other journeys were closely linked with his friends in London, particularly those into North Kent. On the other hand, some of the longer ones seemed to have been undertaken purely for botanical purposes. Such were the journeys into parts of Kent and East Sussex; into Hampshire; into Wiltshire and Somersetshire; the two northern journeys; and the ones into Essex and Cambridgeshire. Some of the excursions in and around London also fall into this category. During these journeys and excursions, Gerard met various people, some of whose names appear in *The Herball*, while other names in the same work are of owners of estates or property, whereon, or in the vicinity of which Gerard made plant collections, but he was not necessarily personally acquainted with any of them.

Gerard's visits to Essex are marked by a singular character—he seems to have kept clear of the central area of the county, and this may have been because his kinsman, John Gerard, Jesuit, was then moving about therein in a fugitive manner, due to his being sought for by the authorities. It seems likely that Gerard visited Essex on more than one occasion. One such journey took him eastwards from Aldgate through South Essex to Tilbury Fort, Horndon-on-the-Hill, and Leigh-on-Sea, where he was acquainted with Richard Rich, of that place, whom he met there. Lord Rich, of Leez Priory, (i.e. Leighs Priory, Little Leighs, Essex), was a landowner at Leigh-on-Sea, to whom Richard Rich was a kinsman. Gerard's reference to "Lee" caused confusion with Leez Priory but Richard Rich was certainly resident at Leigh-on-Sea, as there he made his Will, and there he died. Gerard's record of his collecting marine plants confirms that Leigh-on-Sea was the locality to which he referred. Additional confirmation follows from an examination of the Will of Richard Rich, wherein James Thwaites is mentioned. Gerard knew a man of that name, whom he met at Great Dunmow, but James Thwaites was apparently not resident there. His presence when Gerard met him, may have been due to his being on a visit to inspect land and property he owned in Great Dunmow. That he did so is attested by the Will of his son and heir John Thwaites, citizen and grocer, who inherited both the land and property on the death of James Thwaites in 1611, in which year he made his Will, being then resident at Dedham, Essex. Thus Richard Rich, of Leigh-on-Sea and James Thwaites of Dedham, were not only mutual friends, but each was a friend of Gerard. It should be added that notwithstanding suggestions to the contrary, Richard Rich was neither an apothecary in London, nor was he a retired member of that profession living at Leigh-on-Sea. The suggestion that he was either of these things arose from his having been confused with John Rich, apothecary of London, who became Apothecary to Queen Elizabeth, but the two men were in no way related. John Rich had a garden in London, and both William Turner and John Gerard were acquainted with the apothecary as well as his garden.

There is evidence in *The Herball* that Gerard may have made a cross-country journey in Essex from Leigh-on-Sea to Witham, Kelvedon and Colchester, which would have taken him through Dawes Heath, near Rayleigh and so to Little Baddow near Danbury. At Dawes Heath, Gerard met a Mr. Leonard, who was probably Lionel Leonard, a resident there by 1597, when his signature was appended to a document. At Little Baddow, Gerard recorded that he found *Sisymbrium polyceratium*, L., as a weed in a field of flax, though his figure of it in *The Herball* depicts a different plant, and the *Sisymbrium* has not been seen since, but the Elizabethan period was one wherein impurity in agricultural seeds was common. The *Sysimbrium* is not indigenous to Britain, and may not have survived more than one season. The cultivation of flax ceased altogether, so that there was no opportunity for a re-introduction of the weed. If Gerard did not accurately identify the weed, at least he was sufficiently observant to detect it, and his record has a certain value accordingly.

It may be that Gerard was in Colchester on more than one occasion, as he was acquainted with several people in and around the town, which, at that time, was still almost contained within its Roman wall. He was acquainted with Thomas Buxton, apothecary there, from whom he may have had intelligence of some medical details recorded in *The Herball*. The first of these is particularly instructive. It concerns William Ram, Notary Public of Colchester, who was for a time Town Clerk, and who successfully treated Mrs. Marie de L'Obel after she had been burned by lightning. It is uncertain if Gerard actually met William Ram, who was sufficiently interested in plants as to publish an abridged version of Henry Lyte's *A Niewe Herball*, which appeared as *Ram's Little Dodoen* "A briefe epitome of the *Niewe Herball*, abridged by W. Ram", (London, 1606). His patient, Mrs. Marie de L'Obel, was the wife of Hugh de L'Obel, merchant of Colchester, whom she survived. Matthias de L'Obel visited Colchester in 1596, and it is reasonable to infer that the occasion for this was to call upon Paul and Marie de L'Obel, who were probably his relatives.

Another reference in *The Herball* links Robert Buxton, with John Duke, M.D., a physician in the parish of All Saints, Colchester,

I *Dipſacus ſatiuus.*
Garden Teaſell.

Fig. VII

Dipsacus sativus, "Garden Teasell", which was grown in gardens "to serve the uses of Fullers and Clothworkers". (JOHN GERARD. *The Herball* (1597) p. 1005.) Colchester, visited by Gerard, was a centre of the cloth manufacture.

wherein he resided. His wife was a cousin of Adam Winthrop of Groton, Suffolk, a brother of John Winthrop, first Governor of Massachusetts, and uncle of John Winthrop, first Governor of Connecticut. Mary Duke, his daughter, married Lawrence Wright, M.D., becoming thereby sister-in-law of Nathaniel Wright, M.D., and John Wright, all of whom were of the family of Wright of Wrightsbridge, Hornchurch, Essex. Thomas Johnson, apothecary, of London, was afterwards acquainted with the three brothers, and was a friend of Nathaniel Wright. Just outside Colchester, Gerard became acquainted with a Mr. Boggis. William Turner had also known a man of that name at Colchester, where, and in the vicinity of which, the family had been settled for some considerable time. It is not necessarily the case that the Mr. Boggis known to William Turner was the same man that Gerard knew, as insufficient detail is at present available to decide the point.

A particularly large land and property owner around Colchester was George Sayer the elder, who owned a brick-kiln at Mile End, not far from the town, of which he was a leading citizen. He was Bailiff on several occasions between 1546 and 1564, and an Alderman from 1541 to 1563, and his most important acquisition was Bourchier's Hall, Aldham, near Colchester, to which his son, George Sayer the Younger, succeeded on the death of George Sayer the elder in 1577. He retained the ownership until his own death in 1596. Depending upon the time of Gerard's visits to Colchester, it may be one or the other of these two men to whom he was referring. Perhaps he knew each of them.

If Gerard used Colchester as a base for further excursions, other places mentioned in *The Herball* were within easy reach—Braintree, Castle Hedingham, Mile End and Pebmarsh, in Essex, and Sudbury and Clare just across the county boundary in Suffolk. It may well be that Gerard's route to Colchester was by way of Great Dunmow and Braintree, rather than through Chelmsford. In Gerard's time, Woodford, in south-west Essex, was within easy reach of London and he may have gone there on a local excursion from Holborn. He was acquainted with Francis Whetmore, of Woodford, who seems to have been a son of Robert Whetstone, haberdasher, of London whose Will was dated 1557 and proved in 1560, which shows that he had property and an estate in Woodford, as well as estates in Kent and Somerset. Whether this fact links with Gerard's collecting areas in those two counties is unknown.

I *Tapſus Barbatus.*
Mullein, or Higtaper.

Fig. VIII

Tapsus Barbatus: Mullein, or Higtaper, which, in Gerard's time, grew on Black-heath, "as also about the Queen's house at Eltham", and near Dartford, all of which places were then in Kent. (JOHN GERARD. *The Herball* (1597) p. 629.)

Gerard's presence in Harwich is less easy to account for. He could easily have reached it as a terminal point from Colchester, but he named no one in connection with his plant gatherings in the vicinity of that place. One may note that Harwich was sometimes a port of call for vessels trading to Russia, and Gerard's presence in Harwich may be related to his early journey to the Baltic countries and Russia.

His journeys to Cambridgeshire could have been by way of Woodford, Great Dunmow, Radwinter, Saffron Walden and so to Cambridge. He was probably in Radwinter between 1593 and 1597, as he visited the Rectory orchard there, but made no reference to the Rev. William Harrison, the former Rector. He had friends in Cambridgeshire—John Marsh, M.D., Nicholas Belson, (c. 1535–1591), and the Rev. George Fuller, Rector of Hildersham. From John Marsh, Gerard obtained information respecting a plant found by Marsh near Heath Hall, Copley, in the West Riding of Yorkshire. It was then the seat of Sir George Savile, Kt., who was never a baronet as has been suggested. He belonged to a different branch of the family of Savile, from that of his namesake, Sir George Savile, Kt., who was created a baronet and succeeded to estates at Thornhill, near Dewsbury, which were westwards of Copley, which was itself situated between Dewsbury and Wakefield. Sir George Savile of Heath Hall, was probably a son of George Savile, whose Will of 1595 showed him to be the owner of land and property between Dewsbury and Wakefield in seven places. John Marsh's journey to that area was apparently independent of that of Gerard. From Nicholas Belson, Gerard learned of the experience of Mr. Mayhew, of Boston, Lincolnshire, who was poisoned, though not fatally, while travelling through the fens. The localities visited by Gerard in Kent were situated, mainly, on, or on either side of the pilgrim's road from the Tabard Inn, Southwark to Canterbury—the old Dover road, which featured in Geoffrey Chaucer's *Canterbury Tales*—and Gerard, at least once, travelled its whole length to Dover itself.

Gerard's botanical work in Kent began between 1569 and 1574, and it seems probable that he made several excursions into the county between 1569 and 1597. It will be convenient here to relate his localities to the Dover road. Crossing London Bridge, he would have passed from Southwark into Bermondsey, where a slight diversion would have taken him to the garden of the Earl of Sussex and to that of Thomas Warner at Rotherhithe. These places were then in Surrey, but continuing his journey he would have crossed into,

Helenium.
Elecampane.

Fig. IX

Helenium: Elecampane. Among other places Gerard found it at Lydd and Folkestone, in Kent, probably during his journey from Dover along the south coast of Kent and Sussex. (JOHN GERARD. *The Herball* (1597) p. 649.)

Kent, proceeding by way of Deptford to Blackheath, where a diversion one way would have taken him to Charlton, and another, on the other hand, to Eltham. From Blackheath, he ascended Shooters' Hill, and so to Dartford, when he could easily reach Crayford Sutton-at-Hone and Farningham, where John Sibbell owned land. Continuing from Dartford, he would have passed next through Gravesend, a convenient point from which to reach Longfield Downs, Southfleet, the home of John Sedley, and Hook Green, the home of William Swanne. In the vicinity of Southfleet, John Bradley had his farm. A diversion from the road between Gravesend and Rochester would have taken him to Cobham Hall, the seat of the tenth Baron Cobham, while Rochester afforded a convenient point from which Maidstone, the home of John Bennett, surgeon, and Cockes Heath could have been reached. Proceeding from Rochester, the next important place was Sittingbourne, and a diversion here led Gerard to the Isle of Sheppey, where he knew of the residences of Sir Edward Hoby, and Lord Cheyne, and where he visited Queenborough. Continuing from Sittingbourne, the next stage was to Faversham, where he had a professional acquaintance in Nicholas Swayton, an apothecary there. At this point the Dover road continued to Canterbury, but Gerard seems to have preferred the coastal road by way of Whitstable, past The Reculvers, and so to the Isle of Thanet, especially Birchington, near which was Quex Park, the former home of Sir Henry Crispe, Kt., and afterwards in the possession of a descendant. Margate, a little distance onwards, was the limit of Gerard's route in this area.

On one occasion Gerard continued along the Dover road from Faversham to Canterbury, and so to Sandwich on the coast, and at another time he travelled from Canterbury onwards to Dover, turning westwards there, along the south coast, to Hythe and Romney, in Kent, and so to Rye and Winchelsea, in Sussex. It was on this occasion he met with the fishwives who supplied him with the seaweeds with limpets adhering thereto. Thus Gerard's areas of plant collections in Kent and East Sussex form a very natural and easily understandable group.

The locality mentioned in south-east Surrey and the adjoining part of Sussex is not easily linkable with any of Gerard's journeys into Surrey. All that is known of it is that he was travelling eastwards through Waterdown Forest from Charlwood Lodge, Surrey, to Eridge Park, Sussex, the seat of Lord Bergavenny, situated just south of Tunbridge Wells and west Kent. It is equally difficult to ascertain when this journey was made, because between 1569 and 1597, three different men held the title of Baron Bergavenny. Henry Nevill had succeeded as sixth Baron in 1535, and died in 1587, when he was succeeded by his cousin, Edward Nevill, as seventh Baron, but he dying soon afterwards in 1588, was succeeded by his son, Edward Nevill, as eighth Baron, who died in 1622. There were thus three different occasions upon which Gerard could have been in Waterdown Forest, namely between 1569 and 1587, during 1587–1588, or between 1588 and 1597.

Gerard's journey to Southampton and Portsmouth, and possibly on to the Isle of Wight was undertaken by a route through Surrey and Hampshire in the course of which he passed through Horsley, in Surrey, and near Odiham Park in Hampshire.

Nearer home, more local excursions took Gerard to Hampton Court, probably by way of Twickenham, whereby he made acquaintance with William Hogan, of Hampton Court, and Richard and Vincent Poynter, of Twickenham. William Hogan may have been at Hampton Court in 1564, but in 1604 a grant with survivorship was made to him, to Anne his wife, and to Charles their son, of the Keepership of the Little Gardens at Hampton Court. William Hogan was still there in 1611 when a warrant was issued to pay him one hundred pounds, as Keeper of the Stillhouse and Gardens at Hampton Court, for planting apricots and sundry choice fruit trees there. Gerard referred both to Richard Poynter and Vincent Poynter of Twickenham for their skill in grafting and fruit growing. Though it has been suggested that Richard and Vincent Poynter were one and the same man whose real name was Vincent Poynter alias Corbet, it should be observed that there was a family of Poynter in that area of Middlesex at this time, besides men of that name in London, including Richard Poynter. No details are at present available of Richard Poynter, of Twickenham, beyond his skill in grafting, to which Gerard referred in 1597. On the other hand Vincent Poynter, gentleman died at Twickenham in 1619, being described in his Will as Vincent Poynter, alias Corbet. A Vincent Corbet was a nurseryman or gardener at Ewell, Surrey in 1581, who may have been identical with the Vincent Poynter whom Gerard knew, but the reason for his change of surname to Corbet has not been ascertained. The descendants of Vincent Corbet, of Ewell in 1581, were surnamed Corbet. The probability seems to be that Richard Poynter and Vincent Poynter were related, and that Vincent Poynter, for some unknown reason, changed his surname to Corbet by 1581.

An interesting excursion in Middlesex took Gerard to Harrow-on-the-Hill and Pinner. A cadet branch of the main line of the family of Gerard of Ince was that consisting of the descendants of William Gerard, of Harrow-on-the-Hill, in Middlesex, where they had an estate called Flambards. They were kinsmen of John Gerard, but, in view of the number of his kinsmen then living, it is surprising to find that there is no reference in *The Herball* to any of them. On the contrary, Gerard in his "Address to the Reader" explains that he was left to complete his work alone. Now, the fathers of some of Gerard's contemporary kinsmen had included men who had reached high office in the State, but they had all died several years before *The Herball* was published, and this may explain why Gerard omitted any reference to his contemporary kinsmen, or to their fathers, and what he meant by saying he was left to finish his book alone. What relations or contacts he had with his kinsmen of 1597 is unknown, but their fathers in some cases had been well placed to advance the interests of John Gerard, but their earlier deaths left him without this possible assistance some years before 1597.

It is difficult to reconstruct Gerard's journey into Wiltshire and Somersetshire, including Bristol, but his visit to that city and to the two counties may have been all one journey undertaken when he visited Bristol Fair. On the way to Bristol he passed through Chippenham, Wiltshire, in the vicinity of which Stephen Bredwell was practising as a physician by 1597. Having attended the Fair, Gerard seemingly journeyed into Somersetshire and may have visited Anthony Hales, at Tickname and John Bamfield, at Harding-ton. He was certainly at a place called "Carey", which may mean Castle Cary, or Lytescary, which lies a little distance from Castle Cary to the southwestward. This raises the question as to whether Gerard ever met Henry Lyte at his home at Lytescary, but one must infer that he did not, as otherwise he would almost certainly have mentioned such a meeting. Gerard's return route to London evidently took him to Wilton House, Wiltshire, the home of the Earl of Pembroke.

One journey into Hertfordshire, appears unconnected with Lord Burghley's interests. It took Gerard to Bushey and Watford, on which occasion he met Robert Wilbraham at Bushey, who may even have accompanied him there from London. He was a member of a Cheshire family of which, more presently.

All that need be said of Gerard's journey to Nottinghamshire and Yorkshire is that only fragmentary references to it occur in *The Herball*, and that it seems to have been made independently of those of either Stephen Bredwell, or John Marsh to those areas. Gerard, however, penetrated as far as York itself, as he mentioned Bishopthorpe on the outskirts of the city.

Rather more complicated are Gerard's records of plants in Cheshire, Lancashire, Westmorland, and on Ingleborough in Yorkshire. The few Cheshire records have come in for criticism, and may date from his early years in that county, but may have been later, as he visited Beeston Castle, some eight miles north-west of Nantwich. In Nantwich itself he was acquainted with members of the family of Wilbraham, and more especially with that of Richard Wilbraham (1525–1613) who, by his first wife, Elizabeth Masterson, who died in 1590, had four sons, of whom the eldest was the ancestor of that branch of the family known as Wilbraham of Nantwich, and the youngest son, Ralph Wilbraham, was the ancestor of Wilbraham of Darfold. Robert Wilbraham, whom Gerard met at Bushey, was a kinsman of these men, but his exact relationship to them has not been established. It is, however, with Thomas Wilbraham, third son of Richard Wilbraham with whom one is concerned here. He followed his eldest brother, Richard Wilbraham, to London, and there, at age thirty-one he married Anne Pierson, at St. Lawrence, Old Jewry, on 26th August, 1586, she being the daughter of Henry Pierson, citizen and vintner of London, who had died in 1583. Mrs. Anne Wilbraham was well-known to Gerard, as he mentioned her in *The Herball*.

The records therein of Lancashire and Westmorland plants were the result of collections in Lancashire by Gerard himself, by an unknown correspondent of his at Lytham in the same county, and by Thomas Hesketh, who was partly responsible for the Westmorland plants, and entirely so for those on Ingleborough, just over the county boundary in Yorkshire. Some of Gerard's Lancashire records have also been criticised, but some were due to Thomas Hesketh, who communicated them to him. The association of these two men was very close, as Thomas Hesketh visited Gerard in London, and Gerard may have visited him in Lancashire, where his travels took him to Piel Island, off the coast at Barrow-in-Furness, where he saw the barnacles that featured in his last chapter in *The Herball*. Thomas Hesketh was the second son of Sir Thomas Hesketh, Kt., of Rufford Hall, Lancashire, who died in 1588, leaving a widow and three sons.

The eldest son succeeded to Rufford Hall, whereupon Lady Hesketh apparently removed to Whalley, which lies to the west of Clitheroe, near a road by which Ingleborough could be reached. Gerard referred to Lady Hesketh and her residence at Whalley in reference to one of his Lancashire plants. If he was not at Whalley himself, the record is almost certainly attributable to Thomas Hesketh when on his way to Ingleborough. Thomas Hesketh communicated to Gerard records of Westmorland plants, including some around Crosby Ravensworth in that county, which, at that time was the seat of Lancelot Pickering, who served the office of Sheriff of Westmorland. He is probably the Mr. Pickering to whom Gerard referred in *The Herball*, and he was probably known to James Thwaites of, Cumberland, whom Gerard mentioned as Mr. Thwaites, who communicated a record of a plant at Crosby Ravensworth to him. This James Thwaites was quite a separate man from the James Thwaites whom Gerard met in Essex, being a member of the family of Thwaites of Unerigg Hall, Cumberland.

In and around London Gerard naturally knew many people, among whom were Nicholas Leate, a Levant merchant, who could also have traded to the Baltic, as he had contact with Poland whence he introduced plants. Gerard was in his company at The Theatre in Finsbury Fields, which was opened in 1576, so that Gerard became acquainted with him between 1576 and 1597. Through him, Gerard may have obtained the facilities which enabled him to send his servant, William Marshall, as a ship's surgeon to collect plants in the Mediterranean regions. Another merchant known to Gerard in London was the French Protestant refugee, John de Franqueville, a native of Cambrai, who was known in 1570 to Pena and L'Obel. John de Franqueville lived in London apparently from 1582 until he died in 1608, intestate, in the Parish of St. Stephen, Coleman Street. He had a son of the same name, so that records relating to John de Franqueville after 1608 relate to the son and not to the father. Gerard was acquainted with Randolph Bull, citizen and goldsmith of London, Clockmaker to Queen Elizabeth, who became Keeper of the Great Clock at Westminster to James I, and he also knew Mr. Fowle, Keeper of the Queen's House at St. James's, Westminster, which means St. James's Palace. Gerard himself collected plants in Westminster near Whitehall Palace, and he had an acquaintance at Westminster in Henry Bunbury (1540–1610), a skilful gardener in Tothill Fields. Mr. Fowle was probably Alphonso Fowle of St. James's in 1601.

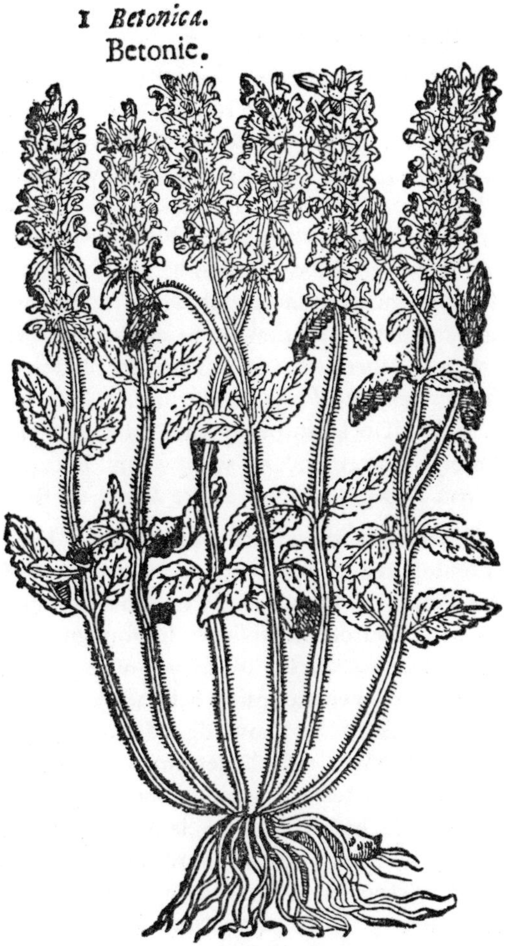

I *Betonica.*
Betonie.

Fig. X
Betonica: "*Betonie*", found by Gerard at Hampstead, Middlesex, near the house
of Sir William Waad, a Clerk of the Queen's Council, from whence he took seeds
for his garden. (JOHN GERARD. *The Herball* (1597) p. 577.)

A little farther afield, Gerard knew Thomas Warner, of Rotherhithe, who was also a fruit-grower, and was known to L'Obel some
time after 1570. The circumstance is of particular interest, as he was
evidently the ancestor of Thomas Warner, of Rotherhithe, who early
in the eighteenth century introduced the Black Hamburgh grape into
England, and had a vineyard there.

Excursions to Hampstead led Gerard to meet various people,
among whom he met there Sir John Hart, as already related. He also
collected plants in the vicinity of the house of William Waad, a clerk
to the Privy Council, who was afterwards Sir William Waad, who
had a country home in Essex. In view of subsequent comments
upon Gerard's botanical work, and his character as an author it has
been thought fit to record the journeys he made in search of plants,
the people he met, and even those with whom he may not have been
personally acquainted. Additionally he carried on correspondence
with botanists and others overseas. Rembert Dodoens was a case
in point: his reference to Francois Pennin, of Antwerp, may have
associations with L'Obel, who also knew him, but Gerard's most
important foreign correspondent, with whom he also exchanged
plants, was Jean Robin, Gardener at the Jardin du Roi, in Paris.

Gerard's supervision for at least twenty years of Lord Burghley's
gardens in London and at Theobalds, his supervision of the physic
garden of the College of Physicians in London, the management of
his own well-stocked garden in Holborn, his foreign correspondence,
his contact and close association with some of the leading botanists
of that time and his own extensive field work clearly show that
Gerard must have possessed a knowledge of plants unrivalled by any
contemporary Englishman, and the testimony of George Baker and
Thomas Thorney, two fellow surgeons and close friends support
that conclusion. He had a wide circle of acquaintances among
botanists, gardeners, florists, and fruit growers. Such a man would
scarcely need to mislead his readers in any book he chose to write,
nor did Gerard do so. His statement that his sources in respect of
The Herball were the works of William Turner, Henry Lyte and
"many other herbals", was correct but he specifically rejected any use
or knowledge of Dr. Robert Priest's translation of Dodoens' last
book. The "many other herbals" were principally the works of
Pena and L'Obel, of Rembert Dodoens, and of Jacob Theodor
Dietrich, of Bergzabern, with lesser assistance from the works, so far
published of Charles de L'Escluse. Besides these, other earlier
authors were cited in *The Herball*, and an "Address to the Reader"

would have become tedious reading had Gerard recited all of them. One is left with the impression that William Turner and Henry Lyte were particularly named because it was to their works that Gerard was primarily indebted for his knowledge of plants. His action in allowing Stephen Bredwell's commendation to be included shows that Gerard approved it, and had nothing to hide in respect of the reference therein to Dr. Priest and his unfinished translation work, but one may note that Stephen Bredwell was apparently the only man of Gerard's acquaintance who had any personal knowledge of it.

The text of *The Herball* affords evidence that Gerard did not blindly follow his authorities, being critical of their conclusions in a number of cases, and did not hesitate to disagree with them when he felt the facts justified his own view. On the other hand, on more than one occasion he indicated that insufficient facts had become available on which a sound conclusion could be based. Biographical details show him to have been capable of speaking his mind, even if controversy ensued, yet despite that, he had an honourable career within the Company of Barber-Surgeons as well as professionally.

In the Proeme to Book I of *The Herball*, Gerard set out the general plan of his work, and indicated how he proposed to end it. This plan was faithfully discharged. The internal evidence in this first book that Gerard was associated in preparing it with Matthias de L'Obel, coupled with its small size compared with Book II, suggests that it may have been commenced between 1569 and 1574. L'Obel's departure for the Netherlands would account for its comparative brevity but Book II provided evidence of renewed contact between Gerard and L'Obel from 1585 onwards.

After his arrival in London in 1570, L'Obel settled in a part of the City, wherein Protestant refugees from France and the Netherlands had been settling for some time. Among them were James Cole, merchant, and James Garrett, apothecary, both of whom were of Flemish origin. L'Obel, Cole and Garrett seem to have been among Gerard's early associates in London. James Garrett practised in Lime Street, wherein James Harvey, citizen and ironmonger also dwelt, Matthias de L'Obel also lived there. Gerard described Garrett in 1597 as "a curious searcher of simples", and also as "my loving friend". Garrett was also a florist devoted to the tulip fancy, and translated the book of Christopher Acosta, though the translation was never published. He grew tulips in his garden in Lime Street, and Gerard recorded that Garrett had been a tulip grower for over twenty years, which shows that he was growing them in London by 1577.   He raised tulips from seed from his own bulbs, and from seeds sent by friends overseas.

James Harvey also had a garden in Lime Street, to which Gerard recorded that he paid a visit and saw mad-apples growing in it. He referred to Harvey as "Master Harvie", which suggests the visit was made and the record of it written before 1582, because on Sunday, 6th May, 1582, James Harvey received the honour of Knighthood at Greenwich.

Gerard's references to James Garrett, and his tulips, and his own visit to Sir James Harvey's garden strongly suggest that Gerard was a visitor to Garrett's garden as well.   It may also be that professional duties brought Gerard to this area of the City, since Lime Street empties, at its southern end into Fenchurch Street, wherein Tobias Browne, citizen and barber-surgeon carried on his practice, and where he made his Will and died in 1573.

Gerard's friendly and appreciative references to James Garrett and to Sir James Harvey occur in Book I of *The Herball*, in which the references to Garrett and L'Obel are cordial throughout.   Since this was the Book in which L'Obel's influence is most evident, the inference may be that Gerard and L'Obel collaborated at an early date in preparing a manuscript work on plants, and certainly before John Norton became interested in Gerard's literary work.   Gerard had received active assistance from Dodoens in respect of figures of two new exotic plants between 1574 and 1580.   John Norton, on the other hand, retained the services of Dr. Priest as a translator from about 1584 until 1590.   His original intention was to publish an English translation of Dodoens' *Stirpium Historiae Pemptades Sex*.

In 1590, Dr. Priest was a member of Section I of the Comitia engaged in preparing the projected pharmacopoeia of the College of Physicians, and this duty, coupled with his professional duties and his translation work may have obliged him to cease translation. Certainly his manuscript was unfinished when he died in 1596–7.

Precisely what occurred in 1590 is at present unknown, but it seems that soon afterwards John Norton became associated with Gerard.   His importation of the wood blocks used in Bergzabern's *Eicones*, could hardly have taken place until late in that year.   He seems therefore, to have embarked about this time on a new project. He may have now abandoned his original intention of publishing Dr. Priest's work, which, as it was unfinished, was of little service to him.   He then turned to Gerard, who, as has been postulated already had some material in manuscript.   This was to be accommodated to figures which Norton would provide, and these were the cuts used for Bergzabern's *Eicones*. If Gerard was lacking in illustrations for his manuscript, such assistance from Norton may have been welcome, but it posed obvious problems if he was now to accommodate his manuscript to the names and figures in Bergzabern's book. One must infer that the names and figures in the *Eicones* of Bergzabern became available to him about 1591, and these figures, but by no means all the names, appeared in *The Herball* (1597), of Gerard, so that it is clear that Gerard effected the accommodation of his manuscript to the figures of Bergzabern between 1591 and 1597. How Dr. Priest was employed during this period one knows not, except that he attended several meetings at the College of Physicians in 1596.

In the early stages of his manuscript, Gerard received considerable assistance from L'Obel, and one must date this early period of close collaboration as having been from 1569 to 1574. Thereafter, L'Obel was continuously absent in the Netherlands until 1585, when, returning to London, collaboration could be resumed, but when it became necessary for Gerard further to collate his work with that of Bergzabern, it seems reasonable to deduce that L'Obel's interest in the manuscript would diminish.

Perhaps it was during the period 1591 to 1597 that the incident occurred in which Gerard brusquely dismissed L'Obel's desire for the correction of errors, with the remark that sufficient had been done in that way, and that L'Obel had forgotten his English. If this incident actually occurred, it hints at the existence of an early manuscript by Gerard, while the incident itself is susceptible of reasonable explanation, if, now that he was definitely committed to publication, Gerard realised that a printer and publisher could not be kept waiting indefinitely for a manuscript.

A comparison has been made of numbers of the names used by Gerard in *The Herball*, (1597), with those used by L'Obel in the *Plantarum, Seu Stirpium Icones*, (Antwerpiae 1583), and with Bergzabern's *Eicones*, (1590). It shows the care that Gerard took in checking earlier names and descriptions, and reveals the probable method which he adopted in assigning the Latin plant-names to the plants he described, and was quite reasonable. Gerard seems first of all, to have used the names of L'Obel as the basis for his work, but if a plant had been left unnamed by L'Obel, but had been named by Dodoens, then his name for it was used, and if neither L'Obel nor Dodoens had named a particular plant, but Bergzabern had done so, then his name for it was adopted. In outline, that seems to have been Gerard's general procedure, and the method hints at the preparation of a manuscript over a period of time. Of course, his complete practice was not quite so simple as described, partly because Gerard was critical of earlier authors, including L'Obel, Dodoens and Bergzabern, and partly because Latin plant-names were undergoing changes in application to particular plants. In cases where subsequent authors adopted a name from the work of Pena and L'Obel, then Gerard used their name, unless he considered a later name more appropriate, and a similar method was followed with Dodoens. On the other hand, if the name of Pena and L'Obel was considered more applicable than that of later authors, then again their name was adopted.

The genus Anemone was known, in Elizabethan times, to consist of wild species, and of horticultural varieties, since it had, by then, become a florists' flower. Gerard noticed the increase in the number of wild species known since Pena and L'Obel published their book in 1570–1571, and alluded to the continual annual increase in the number of garden varieties. He noted that Dodoens described nine plants as Anemone in 1583, which, in fact, they were, and said that he grew a larger number in his Holborn garden. He had thereby a close practical acquaintance with the genus. Bergzabern's figures of Anemones in 1590, were not all reproduced as such by Gerard in 1597. While the majority were retained under Anemone, the remainder were transferred to Ranunculus where they quite properly belonged. Here is a clear case in a critical family of plants, of Gerard's ability to correct the findings of earlier authors, and this occurred in Book II of *The Herball* wherein L'Obel was unable to assist as freely as he had done in Book I. Similar cases are discoverable in *The Herball*, so one should regard Gerard as being, in his own time, a competent botanist.

Throughout the medieval period instances occurred of changes in the application of Latin plant-names to particular plants, this process continuing into Elizabethan times. In early medieval times the vernacular name setwall was applied to an exotic plant, *Curcuma zedoaria*, where roots were imported from eastern countries. By Elizabethan times the same vernacular name was being applied to a species of Valerian, but in the entry relating to it in *The Herball*, Gerard carefully pointed out the earlier application of the name setwall to *Curcuma zedoaria*. It will be apparent that the preparation of his book posed problems for him, which could only be solved by research, and that he did not shrink from undertaking it.

I *Verbena communis.*
Common Vervaine.

Fig. XI

Verbena communis: Common vervaine. Gerard noticed it grew "in untilled
places neere unto hedges, high waies and commonly by ditches everywhere".
(JOHN GERARD. *The Herball* (1597) p. 580.)

69

A comparison of Dodoens' book with *The Herball* shows that Gerard's book was certainly not a direct translation of the *Stirpium Historiae Pemptades Sex*. Gerard's style is individual. In the case of the more commonly occurring plants, almost no description was given, Gerard assuming that the reader would be familiar with them. His text was certainly coloured by material from Dodoens, and it has been indicated that this was inherent in the method adopted for the preparation of the manuscript. Gerard was indebted to Dodoens indirectly through Henry Lyte's book, directly from Dodoens' own publications, and to some extent by direct correspondence with him. Since the *Stirpium Historiae Pemptades Sex* contained material from three earlier works of the same author, one cannot exclude the possibility that Gerard had access to them. If such was the case he had even less cause to need Dr. Priest's translation of Dodoens' last book of 1583. An instructive circumstance bears on this point. Gerard recorded that he found *Gentiana cruciata* in a pasture at Little Rayne, near Braintree, Essex, but the identification is inadmissible since that species is not indigenous to Britain. In Sussex, he recorded *Gentiana verna, L.* as occurring there, but it has been suggested that *Gentiana pneumonanthe, L.* was intended. The plant called *Gentiana pneumonanthe* by Gerard was probably *Gentiana amarella, L.* In solving these nomenclatural problems Gerard had little help from Dodoens' book of 1583, as only one species of Gentiana was described therein, and that was *Gentiana cruciata, L.* On the other hand, the *Stirpium Adversaria Nova* of Pena and L'Obel was of more service, since the authors described five gentians. The first was *Gentiana cruciata, L.* for a figure of which the reader was referred to "Dod. 224", which could not apply to Dodoens' as yet unpublished *Stirpium Historia Pemptades Sex*, (1583), wherein that species is described in Chapter 19, p. 340. Hence Pena and L'Obel were referring to Dodoens' earlier book: *Florum Et Coronarium*, etc., (1568), a work that Gerard may have seen. It is clear that if he had wished to do so, Gerard was able to draw upon Dodoens' works published between 1566 and 1583, and that was his position before Dr. Robert Priest came to London in 1584 or began his translation work. Gerard had certainly been in direct correspondence with Dodoens before 1580, when Dr. Priest's translation work had not even begun.

Besides L'Obel, Dodoens and Bergzabern, Gerard drew upon Charles de L'Escluse, and to some extent upon Jaques D'Alechamps, and Joachim Camerarius the Younger. Dr. B. Daydon Jackson referred to a copy of *The Herball* in the British Museum, which was formerly in the possession of James Petiver, and contained manuscript notes by him, wherein he recorded 139 references by Gerard to Charles de L'Escluse, and an unspecified number of others to Bergzabern, though they were to the plants only, and not to the figures.

Gerard utilised two methods by which to refer to the *Stirpium Adversaria Nova* of Pena and L'Obel. Following what it seems was the contemporary usage, he referred to that work, on some occasions, by the name of the senior author only, and it has been commented upon that he followed this usage in the cases of the plants which L'Obel found at Bristol in 1571. On other occasions, especially in regard to their joint experiments in which animals were used, both authors were cited. It would be unwise to infer from these practices that any discourtesy was intended to L'Obel. Rather it hints that there existed a manuscript work on plants, written at different times over a period of years, in consequence of which first one method of citation was used, and the alternative method on other occasions. The references to L'Obel throughout *The Herball* were consistently appreciative and friendly.

It is much to his credit that Gerard paid particular attention to the vernacular names of plants, which he collected from the country people he met during his extensive excursions in search of plants. In this field, his work has proved invaluable, and his pursuit of it was evidently a continuation of the work begun by William Turner on identification, from which Gerard may well have drawn his inspiration and enthusiasm for it. In an age when credulity was still common, it cannot be held that Gerard was more credulous than his contemporaries. It is clearly the case that he was at pains to ascertain the medicinal or other uses of indigenous and exotic plants, more than once recording his inability to find any record of useful properties, especially in the case of some newly introduced exotic plants. On the other hand, he noted that some of these new importations possessed decorative qualities, and the contents of his own garden showed a mixture of medicinal, economic and purely decorative plants. It marked an important stage in the evolution in England of ornamental plant cultivation. He commented upon the number of ornamental plants to be seen in London gardens, and neither florists' flowers, fruit or vegetables escaped his attention.

Some few illustrations in *The Herball* exhibit plants displaying abnormal development. They depict proliferation or complete foliation of floral organs. Though it was realised that these developments were departures from the normal, the true explanation of them was, of course, unknown in Elizabethan times. Some of these figures have been reproduced from the *Eicones* of Bergzabern, but one or two were provided by Gerard, from material collected in the north of England, or supplied to him by James Cole.

The six Indices at the end of the book are detailed, lengthy, and performed, as Gerrard indicated they would be, in the Proeme to Book I. Each index appears to have been the work of Gerard himself, their titles being as follows:

1. *Index Latinus copiosissimus stirpium in hoc opere I. Gerardi descriptarum* pp. i–xxi.

2. *Index Herbarum hoc opere contentarum, quibus Pharmacopolarum officinae*, pp. xxi–xxvii. *Barbari et Arabes utuntur.*

3. *Nominum et Opionum Harmonia et concensis*, pp. xxviii–xxxiv.

4. A Table of all such English names (as) are attributed unto the Herbes, Shrubs and Trees mentioned in this Historie (in blackletter), pp. xxxv–xliv.

5. A Supplement or Appendix unto the general Table, and to the Table of English names gathered out of ancient and printed Copies, and the mouths of plaine and Country people. (Some entries herein are in black-letter), pp. xxxv–xlvi.

6. A Table wherein is contained the Nature, Vertue and Dangers of all the Herbes, Trees and Plants of the which are spoken in the present *Herball*, pp. xlvii–lxxi.

At this point, the colophon brought to an end the truly monumental volume of Gerard. The titles of the Indices have been reproduced since little attention has been paid to them. William Bullein's book, *Bullein's Bulwarke of Defence*, had contained an Index of the medicinal uses of plants, and Gerard's second index is on similar lines. His fourth and fifth indices have been cited in philological studies of the English language, and the fifth index is notable also for its references to the fact that Gerard had access to manuscript, as well as printed herbals in the course of his botanical studies. This had a direct bearing on the Latin plant-names he employed.

Though these indices have been said to be faulty, so far as they have been tested they were found to be workable. The Latin plant-names used by Gerard should be seen in proper perspective. The invention of printing with movable type in Western Europe about 1450, led to the production of the scientific incunabulae, wherein the texts of Greek, Roman and the principal medieval writers were reproduced by the close of the fifteenth century, mostly in Continental presses. The sixteenth century began with the production of herbals derived from medieval texts, and soon afterwards by commentaries on the classical and medieval authors. These early printed herbals derived from medieval texts bore some resemblance to them in appearance, and naturally utilised the Latin plant-names occurring therein. The importation of new exotic plants from the American continent, Africa and the Far East made botanists aware that, in their day, the Greek, Roman and medieval authors had not been acquainted with plants outside of the Mediterranean Region, parts of Western Europe, and parts of the Near East. In the sixteenth century, there was no standard nomenclature, nor even a generic concept in the modern sense, though a study of the Latin plant-names of Greek, Roman and medieval times leads to the conclusion that such a concept was very slowly taking shape. The primary need was that of indentification—to assign to the plants of Western Europe the correct name, if such existed, that the Greek, Roman and medieval writers had used. Such was the significance of William Turner's work from 1538 to 1568.

Gerard's birth took place towards the close of the first half of the sixteenth century, a period during which the first printed herbals were produced in England, exemplified by those of Richard Banckes and his successors, and these were derived from the Middle English herbal which has been named *Agnus Castus*, and reconstructed from the medical manuscript X90 at Stockholm, and its related manuscripts. Gerard acknowledged his indebtedness to William Turner's books for his knowledge of British plants, and their Latin plant-names. There can be no doubt but that Gerard had a high regard and respect for William Turner and his work. Gerard also made use of the *De Stirpium Historia*, (1542), of Leonhard Fuchs, wherein the Latin plant-names clearly reflect those used in medieval times. The Latin plant-names in the *Book of Simples*, in William Bullein's book of 1562, are entirely those used in medieval times. It is consequently quite clear that these were the Latin plant-names with which Gerard became first acquainted, and he learned more of them when, later in life, he was able to have access to manuscript herbals, and their early printed derivatives. Many of these were preserved in one way or another, by subsequent authors, including Gerard himself. It was inevitable that it should be so, and, when twenty-one years after Gerard's death, Thomas Johnson much enlarged and amended *The Herball*, he, too, maintained, unaltered, large numbers of Gerard's plant-names.

Gerard had no illusion that his work was perfect. He referred to this in his address to the reader, wherein he mentioned it was not free from errors for the reasons he gave there. The Proeme to Book III referred to his difficulties with the figures he needed to illustrate the book, which confirms that some of the cuts were provided at his own expense.

It is unfortunate that the last chapter in *The Herball* has been selected as a basis for assessing Gerard's merit. It was not concerned with plants, but with the Barnacle Goose, concerning which Gerard's remarks have been misunderstood·

The myth goes back to remote times, and was known to the Phoenicians. Mr. Marcus Woodward has usefully summarised its history, pointing out William Turner's doubtful acceptance of its truth. Pena and L'Obel very briefly reproduced the myth only, and William Bullein declined to discuss it. Thomas Johnson, subsequently, added to it.

In this chapter, Gerard discussed three separate matters. A careful reading shows that he was treating here of the Barnacle Goose, the barnacle, and a limpet-like animal found adhering to seaweeds, and he showed an interest in the barnacle and the limpet-like animal as objects of natural history. The Barnacle Goose, (*Branta leucopsis*, Bechstein), is a regular visitor to Britain, mainly to Western Scotland, especially the Solway Firth, to the Inner and Outer Hebrides, and to Ireland. Giraldus Cambrensis, (1147–1222) completed his *Topographia Hibernica* in 1187, wherein he remarked on the Barnacle Goose, though it had been known long before his time. As indicated earlier, he was a descendant of an earlier collateral branch of the family from which Gerard also descended.

The myth confused the bird with the barnacle. Gerard correctly stated that the bird occurred in the North of Scotland and the Orkney Islands. Its appearance there was due to the fact of its being on passage from Scandinavia to the western areas already mentioned. Gerard noted the contemporary vernacular name of the bird—the brant goose, and the local Lancashire name, tree-goose, of which he probably learned during his visit to Piel Island, off the coast of Barrow-in-Furness. But he was little concerned with the bird, probably because he never saw it. At Piel Island he did see barnacles, and probably this is what he was referring to when he said " . . . what our eies have seene, and hands have touched we shall declare". Evidently he both saw and handled barnacles, (*Lepas anatifera*), even though he reproduced the mythical origin of the bird from the animal. It was commonly believed among Elizabethan seamen. Finally, Gerard actually examined a mollusc.

The seaweeds, with the adhering limpet-like molluscs, secured during his journey from Dover to Romney from some fishwives, he conveyed to London. The seaweeds were a species of *Fucus*, and the molluscs adhering to them were similar to limpets found in Guernsey and Jersey. Evidently Gerard was already familiar with them. He examined the mollusc adhering to the seaweeds, and found within the shell an "animal in all stages from shapeless lumps to fowles", the shell being half-open, and the "fowle" ready to fall out. The word "fowle" should here be understood to mean animal, and not bird. In this sense, Gerard's conclusion that the shells contained "Fowles called barnacles" was correct. He had at least examined the animal even if, as Mr. Marcus Woodward has observed, his language was ambiguous. On the facts here set out, it must be clear that Gerard has been quite unfairly judged.

His observation of the appearance of the animal, and its resemblance to a bird was by no means new, as it was this resemblance that gave rise to the myth. As a surgeon, Gerard was capable of distinguishing a bird from an animal, which in the above case he seems to have done, but his reproduction of the myth was of a belief then common in Lancashire and among Elizabethan seamen.

His field work over wide areas of England, and the conduct of his own garden, provided Gerard with a first-class knowledge of indigenous and exotic plants, and enabled him to acquire some ability as a taxonomist. His friends and acquaintances aided his field work, and provided seeds or plants for his garden. Those named in his book have been noticed, and he was highly esteemed by his professional colleagues. All these men and women have been traced in contemporary records, and Gerard evidently enjoyed their confidence and respect. Such would hardly have been the case had he borne during his lifetime the reputation attributed to him by later generations who knew him not.

As Gerard dated his Address to the Reader on 1st December, 1597, and as his engraved portrait is dated 1598, it would seem that *The Herball* was published only just in time for Lord Burghley to receive a copy of it. His death on 4th August, 1598, brought to an end an association of at least twenty-five years in horticultural pursuits, during which new exotic plants had been introduced, and certainly, in some cases, distributed. In the same year Gerard was appointed an Examiner of candidates for admission to the Company of Barber-Surgeons.

Elsewhere in the City of London in 1598, John Stow (1525–1605), was writing his book *A Survey of London*, at the age of seventy-three, in which he referred to some of Gerard's acquaintances. He mentioned the memorial, then existing, to Sir James Harvey, in the church of St. Dionys Backchurch, and referring to St. Swithin's Church, Cannon Street, he noted that on its north side was "a fair and large built house", formerly in the possession of the Prior of Torington, Sussex, but occupied in 1598 by Sir John Hart, whom Gerard had met at Hampstead. There was a "fair garden" on the west side of the house. In the parish of St. James, Garlickhithe, he referred to a brewery, then owned by Richard Platt, and mentioned a shop at the end of Soper's Lane, kept by a woman who sold seeds, roots and herbs. Finally, of the building which was then St. Paul's Cathedral, Stow referred to the memorial in it to Sir Francis Walsingham, whose garden at Barnes, Surrey, Gerard had visited.

A second catalogue of the contents of his Holborn garden, was published by Gerard in 1599, of which Dr. B. Daydon Jackson pointed out that it was a better and more clearly printed edition than that of 1596, probably for the reason that the garden was well known, the earlier issue having been for private circulation. The title of 1596 was retained, but beneath it was the printer's device: the symbols of Mercury, flanked by two cornucopiae, against a landscape. Below that, the colophon read: *"Londoni, Ex Officina Arnoldi Hatfield, Impensis Joannis Norton, 1599"*. Verso, of the title-page, appeared the armorial bearings and motto of Sir Walter Raleigh, to whom the dedication was addressed. A Latin quotation occurred beneath the arms and motto. At the end was the same attestation by L'Obel that he had seen all of the plants named in the Catalogue growing in Gerard's garden. It was now dated "July, 1599".

The Library of the British Museum (Natural History) has a copy of this catalogue, which was formerly in the possession of Matthias de L'Obel, wherein this attestation is struck through leaving the word "Attestor" untouched. Then appears a manuscript entry in

76

Coriandrum.
Corianders.

Fig. XII

Coriandrum: "*Corianders*", sown, in Gerard's time "in fertil fields and gardens" and "doth come of it selfe from time to time in my garden", though he had sown it but once. (JOHN GERARD. *The Herball* (1597) p. 859.)

L'Obel's handwriting "*Matthias de L'Obel haec esse falsissima*" which was undated. Years later, this copy came into the hands of James Petiver, F.R.S., who wrote on the title-page "*Ex dono generosi D. D. Reynardson*", an entry which seems to refer to Jacob Reynardson, (1652–1719), the father of Samuel Reynardson, F.R.S., (1704–1797), of Holywell Hall, Lincolnshire. Each leaf is separately mounted, some leaves being much damaged. When L'Obel thus retracted his attestation is unknown, but it was after 1599, since throughout *The Herball* there is no indication of any rift in relations between Gerard and L'Obel.

A circumstance of 1599 was an order issued on 1st August by Queen Elizabeth for the delivery of arms from the Companies of the City of London, in consequence of which Thomas Thorney, then one of the Wardens of the Barber-Surgeons Company, and a friend of Gerard, lent to him a corslet, a headpiece, a sword and a dagger.

Gerard's visit to Wilton, Wiltshire was followed by a more official one in 1599 by William Gooderons, who has been sent there by Queen Elizabeth to attend the Earl of Pembroke at Wilton House. On 19th September, 1599, the Earl wrote to Her Majesty returning thanks for Gooderon's successful treatment of his complaint, and begged leave for him to remain for a further fourteen days, after which he would see to it that Her Majesty's kindness would enable him to devote himself to her service in gratitude.

William Bourne died during his term of office, in 1601, as Master of the Company of Barber-Surgeons, and on 27th October, 1601, an Order was passed to the Masters of the Company and to Messrs. Thomas Bird, Richard Wood, John Iszard, Thomas Thorney, William Martin and John Gerard to report on Friday next, at 6 a.m. to go on search. This was one of the periodical searches of the premises and practices of members of the Company carried out to ensure the maintenance of a high standard of professional competence, and on 30th March, 1602, Messrs. Christopher Frederick, Thomas Thorney, William Martin, John Peck, John Gerard and Joseph Fenton were ordered to meet at 8 a.m. at Lyon Quay to go thence to "my Lord Admiral", (Lord Howard of Effingham), to complain of Robert Derham for contempt in refusing Her Majesty's imprest. Lyon Quay, situated on the Thames between Dark House Lane and Botolph Wharf, off Thames Street, was one of the Legal Quays for the discharging of goods appointed by Act of Parliament in 1559.

Later in the year, on 2nd November, 1602, it was ordered that "the Committee for Mr. Gerard's garden", shall this afternoon meet at the Hall, "to consider of the report for a Garden for the said Mr. Gerard". This is the last known reference to the proposed garden in the Company's records. Gerard's selection as a member of the two missions of 1601 and 1602 testifies to his reputation among his professional colleagues, of whom Thomas Thorney and William Martin were among his close friends. Thomas Thorney lived in the parish of St. Andrew, Holborn, while William Martin, who was also acquainted with Stephen Bredwell, practised as a surgeon in the Parish of St. Mary-the-Virgin, Aldermanbury, London. Joseph Fenton, another member of the mission of March, 1602, lived, for a time, in the same parish in 1593, but later practised surgery, in the Parish of St. Bartholomew-the-Less, Smithfield, close by. There he died in 1634, and was perhaps, the surgeon of that name who was approved by the College of Physicians to administer inward remedies. Both William Martin and Joseph Fenton practised their profession quite near the Company's Hall, and were no great distance from John Gerard's home in Holborn.

A controversy arose in 1604, between Gerard and Christopher Frederick, the nature of which is unknown, but one may notice that Frederick was a member of the Committee for the proposed garden. The dispute was referred for settlement, on 12th June 1604, to a Committee of the Court of the Company, which suggests the disagreement was concerned with a matter of policy. During 1604, William Clowes died, one of Gerard's oldest friends, whom he had assisted in the edition of his book published in 1591.

The House of Tudor came to an end in 1603, with the death of Queen Elizabeth who was succeeded by James VI of Scotland, who became James I of England, the first of the Stuart monarchs. By 1604, Gerard had been appointed Surgeon and Herbalist to His Majesty, since he is so styled in a document dated 14th August, 1604, at Whitehall, recording that Queen Anne of Denmark, the consort of James I, had granted to John Gerard the lease of a garden plot adjoining Somerset House, in the Strand, on condition of his supplying her with herbs, flowers and fruit. Gerard held the lease for only a short time, as he transferred it in 1605 to Sir Robert Cecil, Earl of Salisbury, second son of his former patron, who, in turn, surrendered it to the Queen. An endorsement of his surrender of the lease was recorded on 27th June, 1611. A little earlier, on 19th March, 1611, a warrant had been issued to pay William Gooderons,

His Majesty's Serjeant Surgeon, five hundred marks for his house adjoining Somerset House. So Gerard had a particular interest in this area.

One may recall here the summoning of the Committee for Mr. Gerard's garden to meet again, after a lapse of years, in 1602, and the subsequent disagreement in 1604, between Gerard and Christopher Frederick one of the members of the Committee, which may have been occasioned by some new development. The site originally proposed for the physic garden at East Smithfield had since been proved unsuitable due to building development. It may be that in 1602, the possibility of another site being available was the reason for the meeting of the Committee, but the disagreement between Gerard and Frederick suggests that there was a divergence of view between them on the matter of establishing a physic garden. Gerard's securing of the lease of the garden plot adjoining Somerset House in 1605 may have been for this purpose, and the facts recorded suggest that he had two good friends in the Earl of Salisbury and William Gooderons to assist him, but his short tenure of the lease, points to his being unable to proceed further in the matter. If this was due to the fact that the Company of Barber-Surgeons felt unable to establish a physic garden adjoining Somerset House, the sequence of events between 1602 and 1605 becomes reasonably intelligible. The garden plot adjoining Somerset House would have been quite as convenient as the site at East Smithfield. Gerard's efforts to establish a physic garden in London, are the earliest known ones of the kind, for which reason it has been thought fit to record them in some detail.

On 24th April, 1604, Lancelot Browne and Martin Schoverus, Physicians to the King and Queen, issued a certificate in favour of the beneficial effects of the Spa waters, (Belgium), for certain diseases. The issue of this certificate was one of Lancelot Browne's last official duties. He had commended *The Herball* in 1597, and his death occurred during 1605. According to custom, Gerard was fined on 26th September, 1605, on declining to accept election to the office of Second Warden in his Company. The order was subsequently rescinded, but after further discussions, Gerard paid the fine on 7th November, 1605, and it was accepted.

He was fined again in 1606 in the sum of eight shillings and eightpence in consequence of a disagreement with John Peck, the Court ordering that they should be friends and all controversies between them ended. The nature of this is unknown, but could not

80

have been too serious, as both men served on the same committee in 1607, since, on 20th July, 1607, Messrs. Thomas Thorney, Richard Mapes, Richard Wood, William Gooderons, William Gale, George Baker, John Peck, Christopher Frederick, John Gerard and Joseph Fenton were appointed Examiners of Surgeons. This was a particularly strong examining body, as all its members, with the exception of Richard Mapes, served the office of Master of the Company between 1591 and 1624, besides which, two members, William Gooderons and George Baker, were Serjeant-Surgeons to the King, and each of them had been Serjeant-Surgeon and Surgeon respectively to Queen Elizabeth.

At the annual elections of the Company on 17th August, 1607, Gerard reached the pinnacle of his professional career, being elected then as Master of the Company. The implications of this are important. Both as a member of the Court, as a Warden, and now as Master, it was an essential part of Gerard's duties to maintain a high standard of professional skill and conduct, and to do all he could to promote the welfare of the profession, and of those engaged in it. Notice has been taken already of his efforts to instruct some of his fellow-surgeons in the knowledge of medicinal plants, and to establish a physic garden the better to carry on such instruction. He had already acted as Examiner of Apprentices. It is quite clear that Gerard was not lacking in a sense of maintaining high standards, and his election to these offices indicated he was a man of honour.

Before the end of the year 1607, both Gerard, and British botany suffered a severe loss by the death of Henry Lyte, to whose *Niewe Herball* (1578), Gerard had been indebted in his earlier botanical work. Another sad event of this year was the death of the Rev. Thomas Newton, one of the commendors both of the books of Henry Lyte and John Gerard, and a third casualty was the death of Thomas Bird, surgeon, of the Parish of St. Faith, which means that he practised in the vicinity of St. Paul's Cathedral, of which St. Faith's was the crypt, as well as the Parish Church.

Reference has been made to Richard Platt, brewer, of the Parish of St. James Garlickhithe in 1598. At his death in 1600–01, he left a son, Sir Hugh Platt, Kt., (1551–1608), to whom he bequeathed land and property in London, Middlesex, and Kent. Sir Hugh Platt had a house and garden at Bishop's Hall, Bethnal Green, Middlesex, and a garden in St. Martin's Lane, London, which, since it was situated in the Ward of Farringdon Within, was not far from Gerard's home in Holborn. Between 1572 and his own death in 1608, Sir Hugh published eleven books in London, the last of which was his *Floraes*

Paradise, (London), H(umphrey) L(ownes), for W. Leake, 1608, a duodecimo work, which had been entered at Stationers' Hall on 18th June, 1608. After the author's death it was eventually reissued with a new title as *The Garden of Eden, or an accurate Description of all Flowers and Fruits, now growing in England, with particular Rules how to advance their Nature and Growth, as well in Seeds and Herbs, as the secret ordering of Trees and Plants. By that learned and great Observer, Sir Hugh Platt, Knight.* An edition of it was issued by W. Leake at London, 1653 (for 1652). The copy described here was the "Fourth Edition, London, Printed for William Leake at the Crown in Fleetstreet, betwixt the Two Temple Gates, 1655". This is in the Lindley Library of the Royal Horticultural Society, London, and contains the bookplate of Arthur Young, F.R.S., and was afterwards in the Library of Edward Ashdown Bunyard, F.L.S. The book begins with an address: "To The Honourable and most perfect Gentleman, Francis Finch, junior, of the Inner Temple, Esquire", and was signed by Charles Bellingham, a kinsman of Sir Hugh Platt, to whom he was closely related, though the nature of it has not been established. Charles Bellingham was of Ewell, Surrey, where he died, his Will, with sentence, being proved in 1618. This address was followed by "The Publisher to the Reader", who also claimed kinship with Sir Hugh Platt, whose "Epistle" to "all Gentlemen, Ladies and all others delighting in God's Vegetable Creatures" occupied pages 11 to 16. An "Alphabetical Table to the Book" followed it, and then came the text, which consisted of short notes, numbered serially, with the names or initials of those who had contributed them, or from whom they had been collected at the end in each case. Among the contributors of these notes on horticultural practises were some friends of Gerard—Edward, Lord Zouche, who had supplied him with seeds, who is, in this book, recorded as having transplanted trees thirty to forty years old on his estate at Hackney, Middlesex, and Richard Pointer, of Twickenham, who is noticed in respect of grafting, and of a particular grafting tool he used. His skill in grafting was noted by Gerard in *The Herball.* Sir Francis Carew, of Beddington, Surrey, is also noticed. Finally, there is a reference to "Mr. Goodman, gardener", Gerard knew a man of this name, whom he described as one of his friends. He referred to him as being of the Minories, near the Tower of London, and the London Subsidy Roll of 1589 recorded him as a resident there, as Thomas Goodman. As a florist, James Garrett, apothecary, was a tulip fancier, but in this book he was mentioned in connection with roses.

Some years later a second part of the book was published, which has been said to be the work of Charles Bellingham. If so, it was written before his death in 1618. It has been noted that the publisher of *The Garden of Eden*, William Leak, claimed to be a kinsman of Sir Hugh Platt, and it must be inferred that if the second part of the book was written by Charles Bellingham that the manuscript passed, after Bellingham's death, to William Leak, who issued it as *The Second Part of The Garden of Eden*, or *An accurate Description of Flowers and Fruits growing in England* . . . "By . . . Sir Hugh Platt, Knight. Never before Printed" (London: Printed for William Leak, at the Crown in Fleet Street, betwixt the two Temple Gates (1660) (for 1659)). It begins with an address "To The Reader", followed by an "Alphabetical Table to the Book", and after that are 159 pages of text. The book ended with a list of books published by William Leak. The text is on the same lines as that of *The Garden of Eden*, but is drawn from the works of Barnaby Googe, Leonard Mescall, and Holinshed's *Chronicle*, as well as from individual contributors and personal records. In numbers of cases, the notes recorded suggested problems, the nature of which is indicated by "quaere". Gerard, it has been noticed, visited Sir Francis Walsingham's garden at Barnes, Surrey, and it is noted in this book that Sir Francis planted apricots on a south wall there. Sir Francis Carew, of Beddington, is referred to again, and Sir Hugh Platt's garden in St. Martin's Lane, London mentioned. There are two references to "Mr. Jarret, the Chyrurgen in Holborn", in respect of carnations, this being, of course, John Gerard, whose surname, at that time was liable to spelling variations of which "Jarret" was one.

A warrant issued at Westminster on 8th February, 1609, to pay to William Gooderons, the sum of four hundred pounds for laying out the grounds of Somerset House. The warrant described him as Serjeant-Surgeon, and it confirms that William Gooderons shared with Gerard a taste for horticulture. The work at Somerset House was carried out for the Crown. In August, 1609, Christopher Frederick, with whom Gerard had once had a difference of opinion was elected Master of the Company of Barber-Surgeons.

On 4th March, 1610, a grant was made at Westminster of the survivorship, to George and Alexander Baker, of the office of King's Surgeon on the surrender of a former patent by the said George Baker. This referred to the patent granted to him by Queen Elizabeth in 1592. Alexander Baker was his son, who was afterwards a magistrate, and Surgeon to James I. About this time the financial position of the Company of Barber-Surgeons was causing concern, because, having elected John Peck, as Master in August, 1610, the Court, on 20th September following, considered a motion from him having the intention of bringing the Company out of debt. It was not to be done easily. Joseph Fenton offered to give freely the sum of twenty pounds, if others would do the same. Some members of the Court followed his example, but William Gooderons said he would think of it, and John Laycock, Thomas Thorney, John Gerard and Christopher Frederick said they would do the like. Not long afterwards the Company lost one of its leading members by the death of William Gale, on 19th November, 1610, at Munken Hadley, Middlesex.

In 1611, a difference between Francis Bilford and John Flint, led the Company on 24th September of that year to order each of them to be bound to the other in twenty pounds apiece "to stand to the Award of Mr. John Gerard and Mr. Richard Mapes". The outcome of this is unknown. The sands of time ran out during the year for two of Gerard's friends and they were running out in his own case and that of others.

William Delaune, M.D., one of the commendors of *The Herball* in 1597, had removed since 1589, from the Ward of Farringdon Within, and at the time of his death in 1611, was of the Parish of St. Anne's, Blackfriars. John Laycock, a sympathiser with Gerard's attempt to establish a physic garden died in 1611 in the Parish of All Saints, Lombard Street.

Early in February, 1612, John Gerard, Surgeon and Herbalist to His Majesty, and a former Master of the Company of Barber-Surgeons, passed away at his house in the Parish of St. Andrew, Holborn, and was buried at the Parish Church on 18th February, 1612. He had been a parishioner for at least thirty-five years, and was survived by his wife, Ann, who had assisted him in his professional duties, and by a married daughter.

George Baker, a firm friend of Gerard for many years, died in 1612, and not in 1600, as has been recorded. The fact is attested by his Will of 1612, wherein he was described as of St. Sepulchre's Parish, London, and in which his estates are recorded. Of those he received in 1592, he died possessed of the Manor of Gapley, Suffolk, and of land and property in London, Berkshire, Dorset, and Derbyshire. Sir Robert Cecil, Earl of Salisbury, who took over Gerard's lease of a garden plot adjoining Somerset House, died in 1612, he being then Lord Treasurer of England.

Of casualties between 1612 and 1631, notice should be taken of the following. Those of 1613 included William Gooderons, John Norton, Hugh Morgan, and Arnold Hatfield. Of these men William Gooderons had been a friend of Gerard for many years, and a fellow parishioner. He will be referred to again presently. John Norton had printed and published *The Herball* in 1597, and Hugh Morgan was an octogenarian when he died at his home in Battersea, Surrey. He had been Apothecary to Queen Elizabeth, and upon his succession to the throne, James I had created him Apothecary Extraordinary. William Turner and John Gerard had mentioned him in their respective books, and Pena and L'Obel had done so even more freely.

Thomas Thorney, a fellow surgeon, fellow parishioner and friend of Gerard, died at his home in Holborn in 1614, and was buried at the Parish Church of St. Andrew, wherein there is a memorial to him. His commendation of *The Herball* in 1597, in verse, deserves special notice for its tribute to its author. Another colleague and fellow surgeon, Thomas Bird, passed away at his home near St. Paul's Cathedral in 1615.

Gerard referred in *The Herball* to Randolph Bull, who was a citizen and goldsmith of London, Clockmaker to Queen Elizabeth, and was appointed Keeper of the Great Clock at Westminster by James I. He carried on business in the Parish of St. Gregory, London, wherein he died in 1617.

John Peck, who had made efforts to improve the financial position of the Company of Barber-Surgeons, died in the parish of St. Antholin, London, in 1618.

There were casualties in the eastern part of the City. They began with the death at his house in Lime Street of James Garrett in 1610, and Matthias de L'Obel, a resident in the same street, died there in 1616. Both men were early associates of Gerard, and were buried in the church of St. Dionis Backchurch.

One other casualty should be mentioned since Gerard mentioned John Hall, a notary public, in the pages of *The Herball*. John Hall carried on that profession in London, and was also a citizen and sadler, and at the time of his death in 1609 he was living in the Parish of St. Mary-le-Bow, in Cheapside.

Though Richard Garth died in 1598, in the Parish of St. Dunstan's-in-the-West, Fleet Street, he left a Will in 1598, in which he expressed a wish to be buried at Morden, Surrey, of which he was Lord of the Manor. He possessed land, called Groutes, near

Croydon, Surrey, on which Gerard had once collected plants. Thus there gradually passed from the scene all those who had been closely associated with Gerard in his professional or botanical work, or with whom he had been personally acquainted. Probably the last was Nicholas Leate, the Levant merchant, who died in 1631.

At one time, Dr. B. Daydon Jackson made extensive enquiries on matters relating to Gerard, his life and activities, and tried unsuccessfully to locate Gerard's Will, and that document has since come to notice. Dr. Jackson reached the conclusion that Gerard, unlike the publisher of *The Herball*, was not affluent when he died, and this was probably true. At the time of writing this paragraph the contents of Gerard's Will are known only partially to the writer of this book. For that reason no discussion of it is possible here. That Gerard's marriage took place between 1569 and 1577, is derived from a consideration of the facts to be recited. At his death, John Gerard was survived by his wife, Mrs. Anne Gerard, whose maiden name has not been ascertained, and by a married daughter, Mrs. Elizabeth Holden. Mrs. Anne Gerard made her Will in 1617, and died in the year 1620 at her home in the Parish of St. Andrew, Holborn. She died possessed of a little property in Holborn, which, if it was all she inherited from her husband, tends to show that Gerard may have been less affluent than some of his professional colleagues. In her Will, Mrs. Gerard mentioned her daughter, Elizabeth, and her son-in-law Richard Holden. She dated the document 29th August, 1617, five years after the death of her husband, and made bequests to the Company of Barber-Surgeons, the children of Christ's Hospital, and to her daughter, Mrs. Elizabeth Holden, and to her grandchildren, Charles Holden, Robert Holden, Anne Holden and Katherine Holden, as also to Richard Holden, her son-in-law. She mentioned the lease of her dwelling in Holborn, and leaseholds in Castle Yard, "held of William Gooderons deceased, late Serjeant-Surgeon to the King". She appointed as her Executors, Thomas Motham, gent., Richard Williams, and William Whitehead, merchant tailor, and the Will was witnessed by John Deane, John Dowse, (who made his mark), and Thomas Tucke (who did likewise), Thomas Deane, and Francis Cleobury, scrivener. The Will was proved on 31st March, 1620 by Thomas Motham and Richard Williams, as William Whitehead had died in the meantime. The Will makes it clear that John Gerard and William Gooderons were not only professional colleagues with a mutual interest and ability in horticulture, they were also tenant and landlord, but nevertheless, close friends for many years.

Part II: 1631—1655

BY THE YEAR 1631, all those men and women whom John Gerard numbered among his friends and acquaintances, especially those named by him in *The Herball* had passed away. Even Stephen Bredwell was in comparative isolation in Wiltshire, and nothing is known of him after 1597.

Since 1595 another set of circumstances had been gradually taking shape, and one's review of them may commence with briefly considering the early life and training of Thomas Johnson, who became an apothecary in London, and served in the Royalist Army in the Civil War which eventually came to pass. He was born in Yorkshire, within ten miles of Selby, in a rural parish situated between that town and Kingston-upon-Hull. He was not born in Selby itself. Thomas Fuller, on the basis of information given to him by a kinsman of Thomas Johnson, as well as a statement by Johnson himself leads to that description of the locality of his birthplace. Of his parentage and early life in Yorkshire little or nothing is known, nor is it known when he was born. The first fact in his life that is on record is that which reveals that he was apprenticed as an apothecary in London to William Bell, who was then free of the Grocers' Company, since apothecaries were still included within that body, though separately from the grocers. Since the unsuccessful attempt of some apothecaries in 1588, to secure separate incorporation, this objective seemed more probable of attainment on the accession of James I in 1603.

After a long struggle, the apothecaries eventually received a Royal Charter in December, 1617, incorporating them as the Society of Apothecaries of London, and the first meeting of the Master Wardens and members of the Court of Assistants took place in the same month. Of this newly established body, John Parkinson was a Charter member, William Bell an original member, and his apprentice, Thomas Johnson, was admitted a Freeman early in 1618 having completed the statutory period of seven years' apprenticeship. That means he began it in 1611, probably early in the year. Fourteen years of age was commonly that at which apprenticeship began, but was sometimes not effected until the age of sixteen years had been reached.

On this basis Thomas Johnson was not born earlier than 1595 nor later than 1597, the balance of probability favouring the latter, rather than the earlier date. He was consequently an infant in arms when John Gerard published *The Herball* in 1597, and he arrived in London, aged fourteen to sixteen years in 1611, probably early in the year, to begin his apprenticeship. As John Gerard died early in February, 1612, Thomas Johnson had no more than twelve months in which he could have made acquaintance with Gerard. Had he done so the meeting would have had little significance, beyond the meeting of an established author by a newly-fledged apprentice. So far as can be ascertained no such encounter between Gerard and Johnson ever took place.

Nor is John Parkinson ever known to have met Gerard. He was thirty years of age in 1597, free of the Grocers' Company and practising in London as an apothecary. In 1618 he was probably practising in the Parish of St. Martin, Ludgate Hill, where he was established in 1607.

The newly established Society of Apothecaries of London natur- ally had teething troubles. Its application for the grant of a Royal Charter had been opposed by the College of Physicians of London, the Grocers' Company, and the authorities of the City of London, and once established as a separate entity relations between the College and the Society were difficult. The period to 1629 was comparatively uneventful. In that year John Parkinson published his *Paradisus Terrestris*, in London, a folio illustrated work, printed by H(umphrey) Lownes and R. Goury. It was entered at Stationers' Hall by R. Goury on 10th April, 1629. It has been properly regarded as more a horticultural than a botanical work, and for that reason it is not further discussed here.

In the same year, Thomas Johnson, accompanied by some fellow- apothecaries, with others, made a botanical excursion into Kent, followed, a fortnight later by another to Hampstead Heath. Of each of these excursions Thomas Johnson wrote in Latin, and published, an account of the localities visited and the plants found. He had also contributed verses to John Parkinson's *Paradisus Terrestris*. At this time he was established in practice as an apothecary at the sign of the Red Lion on Snow Hill, London, and had been there since 1626 and perhaps earlier.

While these events were going forward, relations between the College of Physicians and the Society of Apothecaries were be- coming strained. The physicians complained that some apothe- caries were attempting to practise medicine, and of the manner in which prescriptions were dispensed. Under their Charter, the physicians were empowered to search the shops of apothecaries, such searches being carried out by the physicians accompanied by a Warden of the Society of Apothecaries. In 1618 the College had at last published its *Pharmacopoeia Londinensis*, a folio volume printed by E. Griffin, and sold by J. Marriott, who sold all the subsequent editions down to 1638. The Preface to the first edition had been prepared by a Comita of the College, of which Francis Herring was a member, he having been, in 1597, one of the commendors of *The Herball* of John Gerard.

Thomas Johnson's circle of friends in 1629, included John Parkinson, John Buggs and Job Weale, all of them practising apothecaries. Parkinson had now removed from Ludgate Hill, and was settled in Long Acre, Westminster, where he had had a garden for several years previously. Buggs and Weale were of the party that accompanied Johnson into Kent in the early summer of 1629.

A case of fatal poisoning occurred in London in 1631, which was taken up by the College of Physicians in 1632, and aggravated its relations with the Society of Apothecaries. In the ensuing discussions, the apothecaries had occasion to indicate that many excellent drugs were not listed in the *Pharmacopoeia Londinensis*, of which a fourth edition appeared in 1632. The College had meantime lodged a formal complaint in 1631 in the shape of a petition to the Right Honourable Philip, Earl of Pembroke and Montgomery, that certain men were practising medicine in London without being licensed by the College, among whom they named John Buggs, who was consequently fined, and, refusing to pay, was imprisoned in the Fleet Prison; but was released soon afterwards. It is unnecessary to detail this affair here, but a consequence of it was that John Buggs decided to qualify as a physician, and graduated M.D. at Leyden on 15th July, 1633, being the second known apothecary to qualify as a physician.

A dispute in November, 1633, within the Society of Apothecaries, spread until it involved Job Weale. It concerned a medicine called Lac Sulphuris, which Weale was found capable of making correctly, and he commented upon the effect upon the final product of the vessel in which it was made. Through Weale, Thomas Johnson became associated with this matter, which did not escape notice by the College of Physicians, who carried out two searches of apothecaries' shops, one of which was that of Job Weale on 11th July, 1634, which explains his absence from an extended excursion in search of plants which was made in 1634 by Thomas Johnson, some other apothecaries, and their apprentices to the west of England.

In consequence of their searches of the two apothecaries' shops, the College of Physicians decided to initiate an inquiry into Lac Sulphuris, which took the form of *Quo Warranto* proceedings in the Court of Star Chamber against a number of named apothecaries, the suit being brought by the Attorney-General on behalf of the College. The defendants were twelve apothecaries, among whom were John Buggs and Job Weale. During the subsequent hearings, John Parkinson and Thomas Johnson were among the witnesses who gave evidence in 1635, and it was part of the case of the Society of Apothecaries to question the physicians' knowledge of the simples in the *Pharmacopoeia Londinensis*, and their ability to compound medicines. The materials used in making up medicines were mainly plant products, and the apothecaries, by their training, had a first-hand knowledge of the plants concerned, though Lac Sulphuris, as it happened, was a mineral preparation. The Court did examine the physicians as to their knowledge of medicinal plants, and the result was such that neither John Parkinson nor Thomas Johnson was examined on that point, but the Society of Apothecaries, in those two men, had available in Court, the most competent botanists then in England. The Court proceedings dragged on until 1639, and need not be discussed further. Instead, one may return to Johnson's activities since 1629, more especially his literary work.

A book entitled *Dainty Conceits* (London, 1630), is credited to him, and he had published an account of the Kentish and Hampstead excursions first in 1629, and again in 1632. He then embarked upon a translation into English of the treatise on gunshot wounds published in Paris some years earlier by Ambroise Paré.

It was at this point that he was approached to edit a second edition of *The Herball*, of John Gerard. The rights of Bonham and John Norton in that book had been preserved. On the death of John Norton in 1612, they passed to Bonham Norton, by whom they were assigned in 1632 to Adam Islip, Joice Norton, and R. Whitaker. These three approached Johnson with a proposal that he should edit a second edition of Gerard's book, but Johnson was already at work upon his translation of Ambroise Paré's treatise, and it had already been entered at Stationers' Hall as long ago as 28th September, 1629, to L. Cotes and R. Young. All the same Johnson undertook the work, completed his editorial duties in twelve months, and presented a copy of the completed work on 28th November, 1633 to the Society of Apothecaries.

90

It will be noticed that Johnson began his editorial duties in 1632, the year in which the fourth edition of the *Pharmacopoeia Londinensis* was published. His work was competent, but drastic, such that the final product was virtually a new book. Gerard's medical recipes were largely deleted, besides other matter, and the space secured was utilised to accommodate new plants, which were so numerous that the descriptions occupied more space than his deletions had provided. A few chapters were entirely re-written; some of Bergzabern's figures were removed, and many new ones introduced, these being obtained from the house of Plantin in Antwerp. The positioning of some figures was adjusted to accord with the descriptions. The result was a folio volume of 2,850 descriptions, illustrated by 2,700 figures, of which 800 represented new species. Numerous corrections to Gerard's text were made. As the title page announced Gerard's book was "much enlarged, and amended". Adam Islip, Joice Norton and R. Whitaker were the publishers of this folio volume, an up-to-date, and very accurate account of the plants then known with indications, in appropriate places of their medicinal value, the text being preceded by an historical review of botanical literature from early times, the whole competently set out by an apothecary and able botanist.

But what was the reason for his hurry in carrying out his editorial duties ? It is true he was already committed to translate the treatise of Ambroise Paré, but he was able to complete it and publish it as *The Works of Ambroise Paré* translated by Thomas Johnson, (London, J. Cotes and R. Young, 1632) folio. So that work must have been well in hand in 1632. His edition of Gerard's book was certainly hurried, and there are signs of it in the text, and at the time he began his editorial duties relations between the College of Physicians and the Society of Apothecaries were acute. Faced with a new and fourth edition of the *Pharmacopoeia Londinensis*, in 1632, and with the prospect before them of possible legal proceedings, the Society of Apothecaries may well have considered it necessary to take action to protect its members. Such protection would include the provision of an up-to-date herbal. Gerard's book was the latest one available, but was becoming out-of-date. The preparation of a completely new one would take time. Such a work was already in hand. John Parkinson was well qualified to write a new herbal and he was at work upon his *Theatrum Botanicum*, aged sixty-two An alternative choice was Thomas Johnson, aged between thirty-five and thirty-seven years, but already committed to some translation work. He had already published the results of his field work in

Kent and on Hampstead Heath, so was well qualified botanically. An edition of Gerard's book offered a rapid way of producing a new herbal, if a competent person could be found to carry out the necessary work. Such might be the background to the approach made to Johnson in 1632, and the possible impending legal proceedings would explain the need for the editorial work to be hurried. It would also give point to Johnson's presentation of the completed work as evidence of the accomplishment of his assignment. His Kentish and Hampstead plants had been named after those in the works of Pena and L'Obel, Dodoens and Gerard, so he was well acquainted with earlier plant names. He made further corrections to them, but as Parkinson subsequently found, he left numbers of others unaltered.

An examination of the names in Johnson's edition of Gerard's book confirms that he maintained unaltered numbers of Gerard's names, besides which by no means all of Bergzabern's figures were removed. Johnson, in his Address to the Reader, apologises for any defects that may occur in his work, pleading the pre-occupation of his "other businesses" in mitigation. The nature of these other businesses is now known, and the reason for his hurry explained. The Society of Apothecaries had a splendid card to play should it be needed.

In the course of his editorial work, Johnson has been held to have anticipated some of the material that appeared subsequently in John Parkinson's *Theatrum Botanicum*, but, while Parkinson was aware of it, his later comparatively mild expostulation concerning it, seems to indicate that he did not view the matter very seriously. He was in fact, rather reticent on that matter.

One point concerning Johnson's "Address to the Reader" cannot yet be explained. Johnson was entitled to criticise Gerard's botanical work, and to set out his own views, and this he did meticulously well, but nowhere did he give credit to Gerard for his earlier corrections. Indeed, he went further, he alleged that Gerard had concealed the fact that *The Herball* was based on a translation by Dr. Robert Priest of Dodoens' *Stirpium Historiae Pemptades Sex* (1583).

This information was supplied to Johnson by an informant whom he did not name, but who, he claimed, had known both John Gerard and Dr. Robert Priest personally. Now, from at least 1626 onwards, if not earlier, Johnson was in practice as an apothecary on Snow Hill, London, which occupied, at that time, a quite different site from the street that now bears that name. If, in 1626, one left Gerard's former home in Holborn, and proceeded eastwards, the road led down to the stone bridge across the Fleet River, and then ascended as a steep winding street until it affected a junction with Gillspur Street, Newgate Street and Old Bailey, this was Snow Hill, upon which Thomas Johnson lived and practised his profession. He was thereby within a short distance of Gerard's former home, and even nearer to St. Andrew's Church, Holborn, where Gerard was buried. It is a curious circumstance that Johnson was vague as to the year in which Gerard died. He put it at 1609, whereas in fact the event occurred in 1612. Of Robert Priest, Johnson observed that he died "before or after" completing his translation work, whereas Stephen Bredwell's commendatory letter showed that the translation work was incomplete when Dr. Priest died, and Gerard's address to the reader gave the date of that event as having been between late in 1596 and before 1st December, 1597.

Johnson's informant cannot be relied upon if he supplied to Johnson material such as this. Clearly Johnson knew little or nothing of Dr. Priest's translation work. He seems in his address to the reader to hint at having once met Gerard, but had he done so, surely he would have recalled the correct year of Gerard's death. Had this temporarily eluded him, his close proximity to St. Andrew's Church offered a quick and ready means to check it. The possible method by which Gerard assembled his material for *The Herball* need not be repeated here, but one may note that nothing is known at present of Dr. Priest's translation work. No copy of it seems to have survived. It is unknown when he started it, or when he ceased to work at it. There is only Stephen Bredwell's testimony that it probably reached an advanced stage, but was never finished. No evidence is so far forthcoming that Gerard ever met Dr. Priest, even though their respective duties at the College of Physicians afforded opportunities for such a meeting. The testimony of Johnson's informant is unreliable and should be rejected. The implication follows that *The Herball* was Gerard's own work, with assistance, especially in Book I, from Matthias de L'Obel, and contributions by Rembert Dodoens, and, in respect of the localities of English plants, from his several correspondents. Johnson's criticisms of Gerard concerned the names of some of the plants he had described, and the positioning of some figures in relation to the descriptions. He alleged Gerard had caused confusion in the identification of plants, such that it was very difficult to resolve them.

Though he meticulously indicated instances wherein he had made corrections, these were not a high percentage of the total number of plants Gerard described. The positioning of figures cannot be laid entirely at Gerard's door. In some cases figures were transposed, due entirely to the fact that in 1597, there was imperfect knowledge of some of the plants depicted, and this persisted for a considerable period afterwards. One must remember that during the twenty-one years that elapsed between the publication of *The Herball*, and of Johnson's edition, no comparable work either in scope or standing was produced in England, but progress had been made in the knowledge of plants and plant-names. The publication of Caspar Bauhin's *Pinax*, in 1623 was particularly important and significant in this connection.

In justice to Johnson it should be observed that he displayed some appreciation of Gerard and his work, commending him for it. The effect of his strictures upon it was such that Gerard was virtually damned with faint praise to succeeding generations, from which he has never entirely recovered. On the other hand, Johnson's anticipation of matter in the *Theatrum Botanicum* of Parkinson was not a serious matter.

A very fair assessment of the respective abilities of John Gerard and Thomas Johnson was made, first by Dr. Richard Pulteney in 1790, and second, by Sir James Edward Smith, between 1814 and 1819. They were truly impartial in their comments upon the history of botany in England. These show that Gerard was considered to be the better botanist, but that Johnson was the better scholar—a view with which Gerard would, perhaps, not have been displeased.

A Will made in 1628, before Johnson's editorial work began, reveals the regard in which Gerard's book was held at the time. The testator bequeathed to "George Peren, barber-surgeon, my yearball known by the name of 'Gerard's Yearball' ". The legatee was George Perin, barber-surgeon of the Parish of St. Bride, Fleet Street, London, in 1633 in which year he made his own Will and died. It was the year so fateful for Gerard's future reputation, so that it is reassuring to find that there were those among Johnson's contemporaries who valued and treasured Gerard's book.

Though Johnson's strictures on Gerard were the first to appear, they were not the last. Johnson based his remarks, according to his own account, on hearsay evidence, and did not disclose the name of his informant. He published his strictures when neither John Gerard nor Robert Priest could defend themselves. This must render them suspect, and they should be rejected as unreliable, but, even as he wrote, there were lying in manuscript in 1632–1633, some other criticisms of Gerard and his work, and to this manuscript Johnson must have had access. Extracts from it were published in 1655, eleven years after Johnson's untimely death from wounds received on 14th September, 1644, during the siege of Basing House in the Civil War, in which Johnson held the appointment of Lieutenant-Colonel in the Royalist garrison.

Matthias de L'Obel paid a visit to John Parkinson's garden in 1615, when Parkinson was resident in the Parish of St. Martin, Ludgate-Hill, where he had been practising as an apothecary since 1607, if not earlier. L'Obel's death occurred during 1616, whereupon Parkinson purchased his manuscript, which remained in his possession until his own death in 1650. These papers included a manuscript work entitled *Stirpium Illustrationes*, upon which L'Obel had laboured during his closing years. The late Dr. C. E. Raven has summarised the chief contents of this work so it is necessary to say only that, after Parkinson's death, extracts from it were published by William How, M.D., under the title: *Stirpium Illustrationes, Plurimas elaborantes inauditas Plantas subreptitiis. J. Parkinsonii rapsodis (ex cordica M.S. insalutato) sparium gravatae. Accurante G. How, Anglo, (Londini, 1655)* 4to. Some years ago, Dr. R. W. T. Gunther found L'Obel's original manuscript at Magdalen College, Oxford, where it reposes in the College Library.

From this work, one learns that, as related, L'Obel visited Parkinson in 1615, which helps to explain Parkinson's purchase of his manuscripts. How's charges against Parkinson in respect of them cannot be justified, and, in any case, they are irrelevant here. What is important are some observations which L'Obel wrote in the manuscript of the *Stirpium Illustrationes*, for he recorded that John Norton, publisher of *The Herball* in 1597, was warned by James Garrett that Gerard's work, particularly in the early chapters, contained errors, and that, in consequence, Norton requested L'Obel to check and correct the placing of pictures, and to undertake other editorial revision. L'Obel claimed to have corrected over a thousand mistakes until Gerard was so irritated that he declined to make further corrections, and made remarks concerning L'Obel's knowledge of English. He spoke of Gerard as one who stitched together patches of other people's works, and elaborated this charge. Later, he roundly accused Gerard of plagiarism. Here, then, is the source of Johnson's strictures on Gerard, yet Johnson gave no hint that he had seen this manuscript.

L'Obel's account hardly tallies with the evidence of *The Herball* itself, wherein Gerard, more than once, termed James Garrett "my loving friend", which he would scarcely have done had Garrett behaved towards him in the manner alleged by L'Obel. The early chapters of *The Herball* are precisely those in which the collaboration of L'Obel with Gerard was closest. They formed the short first Book, which may have been assembled between 1569 and 1574. Norton could not have invited L'Obel to supervise the positioning of figures, and to carry out editorial duties until 1591, and Gerard's manuscript was then incomplete. The alleged incident concerning an irritated Gerard has been explained, and is clearly of small moment.

At this point one should recall L'Obel's cancellation in manuscript of the printed attestation in his copy of the *Catalogue of the Plants in Gerard's Garden*, issued in 1599, which seems to link with the remarks written by L'Obel in his manuscript of the *Stirpium Illustrationes*. The cancellation and the strictures upon Gerard may well have been made about the same time, and may be dated between 1599 and 1616. They may even have been carried out after Gerard's death in 1612.

The cause of the hostility towards Gerard is unknown, but on the facts available, L'Obel's testimony as to his part in *The Herball* needs to be treated with caution, since it does not accord with that provided by the book itself.

The general impression afforded by this study of Gerard's life and work is that of a gentleman, and a competent and successful surgeon, esteemed by his fellow surgeons for his professional ability and his knowledge of plants. He was an able and widely travelled field botanist in England, and a skilful cultivator of indigenous and exotic plants, besides striving to instruct fellow surgeons in a knowledge of medicinal plants, and to establish a physic garden in London to aid in this work. He retained the patronage and confidence of Lord Burghley for at least twenty-one years, and his merits were appreciated by Queen Elizabeth and James I, who honoured him with the title of Surgeon and Herbalist to His Majesty. William Clowes, his friend for many years, and the author of some of the best Elizabethan works on surgery, wrote approvingly of Gerard, and his book. *The Herball* should be regarded as his own work, the product of many years of study, field work, and observation of plants in cultivation. Therein, he reviewed the Latin plant-names used by earlier authors, effecting corrections thereto in a number of cases, in which sound judgment was displayed. Additionally, his study and record of vernacular plant names has proved invaluable, and should be regarded as a continuation of the earlier work in that field of William Turner. He made no claim to scholarship or to specialist knowledge, nor did he consider that his work was free from error, and certainly, as he realised, in a work of such magnitude, carried on while he was yet earning his living as a practising surgeon, some errors were bound to creep in. Much has been made of those discerned by later students of Gerard's book, but by no means all should be laid at Gerard's door, as an examination of some of them has disclosed. Viewed in this light, Gerard, in his day, performed yeoman service to botany and horticulture in England. As a Member of the Court of Assistants, and eventually as a Warden and Master of the Company of Barber-Surgeons, Gerard had been trained in the need to maintain high professional standards of conduct and practice, and this is evident also in his botanical work.

His statements regarding the men and women mentioned in *The Herball* have all been found perfectly correct. He was clearly an honest and upright man, and Thomas Thorney's tribute to him in verse was fully justified, and has received inadequate notice. It was especially valuable, because it came from one who was a fellow-surgeon, a near neighbour and fellow-parishioner, and also a close friend. Thomas Thorney knew Gerard extremely well. *The Herball* was really the last of that class of book to be published in the sixteenth century. Thereafter, a new period opened, so Stephen Bredwell's words regarding Gerard's authorship, that he came last but by no means the least, are particularly appropriate.

———

In conclusion, it is an especially pleasant duty to record appreciation of the facilities afforded for biographical and bibliographical research by the Essex Record Office and the Chelmsford Public Library, both in Chelmsford, Essex, whose respective Essex records and collections have been of particular value. Grateful acknowledgment is made to Mr. Philip W. Foster by whom the illustrations were made and supplied. They are reproductions of herbs figured in *The Herball*.

List of Works Consulted

S. A. ALLIBONE *Critical Dictionary of English Literature* (New York, 1902).

— *Catalogue of Books*, etc. in the Library of the British Museum, (Natural History), 5 Vols. (London 1903–1915).

AGNES ARBER *Herbals, Their Origin and Evolution.* (Cambridge, 1928).

SIR GEORGE JOHN ARMYTAGE, BT. *Middlesex Pedigrees* ... 1551. Pubs. Harl. Soc. 65 (London, 1914) pp. 6 and 33.

D. A. BANNERMAN *The Birds of the British Isles*, Vol I (Edinburgh and London, 1957) pp. 270–284. Plate 22.

W. B. BANNERMAN *The Registers of St. Mary the Virgin*, Aldermanbury, London. Part I, Pubs. Harl. Soc. 6 (London, 1931) pp. 44–62, and 55–58.

W. B. BANNERMAN *The Visitations of Kent* Taken in the Years 1530–31 and 1574. Part I Pubs. Harl. Soc. 74 (London, 1923) pp. 19 and 30–31.

W. G. BENHAM *The Oath Book*, or Red Parchment Book of Colchester (Colchester, 1907).

G. T. BOULGER "History of Botany in Essex" in *Essex Naturalist* 11 (1900) pp. 57–58, 169–184, 229–236.

J. BRITTEN and G. L. BOULGER *Index of deceased British and Irish Botanists* Ed. 2 (London, 1931).

GOSTA BRODIN *Agnus Castus:; A Middle English Herbal* (Upsala, 1950).

— BURKE *Burke's Peerage, Baronetage and Knightage* (Ed. 103) (London, 1963).

SIR BERNARD BURKE *A Genealogical History of* ... *Extinct Peerages in the British Empire* (London, 1883).

SIR BERNARD BURKE *The General Armorial* (London, 1884).

J. L. CHESTER *The Register Booke of St. De'nis Backchurch Parishe* (City of London) Pubs. Harl. Soc. 3 (London, 1878).

MILLER CHRISTY W. W. Porteous and E. Bertram Smith: "Some Interesting Essex Brasses" in Trans. Essex Archeol. Soc. N.S. 6. (1906) pp. 22–67.

W. S. C. COPEMAN *Doctors and Diseases in Tudor Times* (London, 1960).

F. G. EMMISON *Wills at Chelmsford* Vol. I (1400–1619) (London, 1958).

MARC FITCH *Index to Administrations in the Prerogative Court of Canterbury* Vol. 4 (1596–1608) (London, 1964) pp. 12, 39, 110.

JOSEPH FOSTER *Alumni Oxonienses* 4 Vols. (Oxford 1891–1892).

JOHN GERARD *The Herball, or a Generall Historie of Plantes* (London, 1597).

MARY ANNE EVERETT GREEN *Calendar of State Papers* (Domestic Series) (Elizabeth) (1591–1601) (London, 1867; 1868 and 1869) 3 Vols.

MARY ANNE EVERETT GREEN *Calendar of State Papers* (Domestic Series) (James I) (1603–1618) (London, 1857 and 1858) 2 Vols.

H. A. HARBEN *A Dictionary of London.* (London, 1918.)

EDWARD HASTED *The History and Topographical Survey of the County of Kent* Vol I (Canterbury, 1708).

MISS T. M. HOPE "References to Essex in 'Gerard's Herball' ", in *Essex Review* 28 (1914) pp. 4–12.

J. J. HOWARD AND G. J. ARMYTAGE *The Visitation of London in the Year 1568.* Pubs. Harl. Soc. 1 (London, 1869) pp. 95.

J. J. HOWARD AND J. L. CHESTER *The Visitations of London, Anno Domini 1633, 1634 and 1635.* Pubs. Harl. Soc. 15 (London, 1880) pp. 39 and 175.

THOMAS JOHNSON *The Herball, or a Generall Historie of Plantes* by John Gerard, Amended and very much Enlarged (London, 1633).

H. W. KEW AND H. E. POWELL *Thomas Johnson, Botanist and Royalist* (London, 1932).

J. H. LEA *Abstracts of Wills in the Prerogative Court of Canterbury*, at Somerset House, London, England. Register Soame, 1620, (Boston, Mass. 1904) p. 98 n. 285.

SIR SIDNEY LEE *Dictionary of National Biography* 21 Vols. (London, 1908 and 1909).

H. S. LONDON AND SOPHIA W. RAWLINS *Visitation of London, 1568* . . . and *A London Subsidy Roll, 1589*. Pubs. Harl. Soc. 109–110 (London, 1963).

ROBERT LEMON *Calendar of State Papers* (Domestic Series) (Edward VI, Mary, Elizabeth) (1547–1580) (London, 1856).

REV. O MANNING AND W. BRAY *The History and Antiquities of the County of Surrey* Vol. 2 (London, 1808) p. 488.

J. MATTHEWS AND G. F. MATTHEWS *Abstracts of Probate Acts and Sentences in the Prerogative Court of Canterbury* Vol I (1620–1624) (London, 1911) p. 126.

J. MATTHEWS AND G. F. MATTHEWS *Abstracts of Probate Acts in the Prerogative Court of Canterbury* (1630–1634) (London, 1902) pp. 229–264.

W. C. METCALFE *The Visitations of Essex* Vol. I, Pubs. Harl. Soc. 13 (London, 1878).

W. MUNK *The Roll of the Royal College of Physicians of London* Vol. I (London, 1861).

J. NICOLSON AND R. BURN *History and Antiquities of the Counties of Westmorland and Cumberland* Vol. I (London, 1777) (pp. 498–499.

A. W. POLLARD AND G. R. REDGRAVE *A Short Title Catalogue of Books printed in England, Scotland and Ireland . . . 1475–1640* (London, 1946).

R. PULTENEY *Sketches of the Progress of Botany from the Earliest Times to that of Linneaus* Vol. I (London, 1790).

REV. C. E. RAVEN *Early English Naturalists from Neckham to Ray* (Cambridge, 1947).

SIR JOHN EDWIN SANDYS *"Education", in Shakespeare's England:* An Account of the Life and Manners of his Age. Vol. I (Oxford, 1916).

MISS C. FELL SMITH *John Dee (1527–1608)* (London, 1909).

SIR JAMES EDWARD SMITH in *A Rees, Cyclopedia* (London, dated 1819), s. v. Gerardia.

S. A. SMITH, M.D., AND L. L. DUNCAN *Index of Wills proved in the Prerogative Court of Canterbury*, Vol. 3 (1558–1583), (London, 1898).

S. A. SMITH, M.D. AND E. A. FRY *Index of Wills proved in the Prerogative Court of Canterbury*, Vol. 4 (1584–1604), (London, 1901).

E. STOKES *Index of Wills proved in the Prerogative Court of Canterbury*, Vol. 5 (1605–1619), (London, 1912).

CHARLES STONHAM *The Birds of the British Islands*, Vol. 3 (London, 1908) pp. 438–441. Plate 163.

J. VENN AND J. A. VENN *Alumni Cantabrigienses*, Part I, 4 Vols. (Cambridge, 1922–1927).

MARCUS WOODWARD *Gerard's Herball: The Essence thereof distilled* (London, (1927) 1964).

THOMAS WRIGHT *The History and Topography of Essex*, Vol. I (London, 1831), and Vol. 2 (London, 1834).

SIDNEY YOUNG *Annals of the Company of Barber-Surgeons of London* (London, 1890).